Yoga Education for Children

With kind regards, ॐ and prem

Swami Niranjan

Yoga Education for Children

Swami Satyananda Saraswati

Yoga Publications Trust, Munger, Bihar, India

Published by Bihar School of Yoga
First UK edition 1985
First Indian edition 1990
Reprinted with corrections 1999

Published by Yoga Publications Trust
Reprinted 2003, 2004

ISBN: 81-85787-33-6
Price: Indian rupees one hundred only

Publisher and distributor: Yoga Publications Trust, Ganga Darshan, Munger, Bihar, India.

Printed at Thomson Press (India) Limited, New Delhi, 110001

SWAMI SIVANANDA SARASWATI

Swami Sivananda was born at Pattamadai, Tamil Nadu, in 1887. After serving as a medical doctor in Malaya, he renounced his practice, went to Rishikesh and was initiated into Dashnami sannyasa in 1924 by Swami Vishwananda Saraswati. He toured extensively throughout India, inspiring people to practise yoga and lead a divine life. He founded the Divine Life Society at Rishikesh in 1936, the Sivananda Ayurvedic Pharmacy in 1945, the Yoga Vedanta Forest Academy in 1948 and the Sivananda Eye Hospital in 1957. During his lifetime Swami Sivananda guided thousands of disciples and aspirants all over the world and authored over 200 books.

SWAMI SATYANANDA SARASWATI

Swami Satyananda was born at Almora, Uttar Pradesh, in 1923. In 1943 he met Swami Sivananda in Rishikesh and adopted the Dashnami sannyasa way of life. In 1955 he left his guru's ashram to live as a wandering mendicant and later founded the International Yoga Fellowship in 1956 and the Bihar School of Yoga in 1964. Over the next 20 years Swami Satyananda toured internationally and authored over 80 books. In 1987 he founded Sivananda Math, a charitable institution for aiding rural development, and the Yoga Research Foundation. In 1988 he renounced his mission, adopting kshetra sannyasa, and now lives as a paramahamsa sannyasin.

SWAMI NIRANJANANANDA SARASWATI

Swami Niranjanananda was born in Madhya Pradesh in 1960. At the age of four he joined the Bihar School of Yoga and was initiated into Dashnami sannyasa at the age of ten. From 1971 he travelled overseas and toured many countries for the next 11 years. In 1983 he was recalled to India and appointed President of Bihar School of Yoga. Since then he has guided the development of Ganga Darshan, Sivananda Math, Yoga Publications Trust and the Yoga Research Foundation. In 1990 he was initiated as a paramahamsa and in 1993 anointed preceptor in succession to Swami Satyananda. Bihar Yoga Bharati was founded under his direction in 1994. He has authored over 20 books and guides national and international yoga programs.

SWAMI SATYASANGANANDA SARASWATI

Swami Satyasangananda (Satsangi) was born on 24th March 1953, in Chandorenagore, West Bengal. From the age of 22 she experienced a series of inner awakenings which led her to her guru, Swami Satyananda. From 1981 she travelled ceaselessly with her guru in India and overseas and developed into a scholar with deep insight into the yogic and tantric traditions as well as modern sciences and philosophies. She is an efficient channel for the transmission of her guru's teachings. The establishment of Sivananda Math in Rikhia is her creation and mission, and she guides all its activities there, working tirelessly to uplift the weaker and underprivileged areas. She embodies compassion with clear reason and is the foundation of her guru's vision.

Contents

Introduction 1

Yoga and Education
1. The Need for a Yoga-Based Education System 13
2. Yoga and Children's Problems 22
3. Yoga with Pre-School Children 25
4. Yoga Lessons Begin at Age Eight 31
5. Student Unrest and Its Remedy 34
6. Yoga and the Youth Problem 39
7. Better Ways of Education 45
8. Yoga at School 50
9. Yoga and Education 57
10. Questions and Answers 65

Yoga as Therapy
11. Yoga for Emotional Disturbances 77
12. Yoga for the Disabled 83
13. Yoga Benefits Juvenile Diabetes 87

Practices
14. Yoga Techniques for Pre-School Children 93
15. Yoga Techniques for 7–14 Year-Olds 101
16. Yoga Techniques for the Classroom 110
17. Introduction to Asana 133
18. Pawanmuktasana Series 139
    Pawanmuktasana 1: Anti-Rheumatic Asanas 141
    Pawanmuktasana 2: Anti-Gastric Asanas 156
    Pawanmuktasana 3: Energizing Asanas 165
19. Eye Exercises 171

20. Surya Namaskara: Salutations to the Sun 176
21. Chandra Namaskara: Salutations to the Moon 182
22. Warrior Sequence 188
23. Relaxation Asanas 193
24. Animal Asanas 196
25. Object Asanas 222
26. Characters and Persons 249
27. Alphabet Asanas 255
28. Asanas Done in Pairs 259
29. Pranayama 264
30. Practical Teaching Syllabus 271
31. Light of Existence Explained 285

Bibliography 290

Index of Practices 293

General Index 298

Introduction

The present book is intended as a guideline for teachers of yoga to children. It is based on the experience of the various authors who have taught yoga to children in widely differing environments for a considerable number of years. The book indicates some of the requirements of children of different age groups, abilities and disabilities, as well as some of the constraints imposed by the teaching environments. Furthermore, the book presents some of the ways teachers have adapted the general yoga practices to suit their own specific requirements and constraints.

The techniques for practice given in the last section of the book may be used as a basis for one who is new to teaching yoga to children. Both novice and experienced teachers alike can adapt these and other yogic techniques to their particular needs. As this book is a compilation of work from different authors and intended to be a reference and guideline, some information may be repeated.

What is yoga?

Yoga is the art and science of living, and is concerned with the evolution of mind and body. Therefore, yoga incorporates a system of disciplines for furthering an integrated development of all aspects of the individual. When we start the disciplines of yoga we usually begin with the outermost aspect of the physical personality, the physical body. Through the

ostures, or *asanas*, the spinal column
joints are maintained in a healthy
assage takes place at the location
many physiological abnormali-
hypothyroid problems, faulty
ther hormonal imbalances.

eathing techniques, are important not only
fresh oxygen and strengthening the lungs but
they have a direct effect on the brain and emotions.
e emotional stability gained through pranayama frees mental and creative energies in a constructive way, and the child exhibits more self-confidence, self-awareness and self-control.

Relaxation, by withdrawing the awareness from the external environment, or *pratyahara*, reduces the stress of daily living experiences. Techniques of pratyahara such as *yoga nidra* affect all aspects of the individual, because physical and mental relaxation through withdrawal of the empirical awareness, and concentration, the focusing of attention, or *dharana,* are important elements of that technique.

Sustained concentration, or *dhyana,* is important for stilling the turbulent mind and channelling focused mental energy creatively. Equanimity in daily life can be experienced and later *samadhi*, the ultimate aim of all yoga practices, is brought about through constant repetition of yogic disciplines. The practice of yoga creates a balance in the total personality. In this book, we will look at the physical, emotional, mental and creative aspects of the personality.

Physical aspect

In this book we will be focusing largely upon the physical aspect, therefore a basic understanding of the major systems is needed.

Supportive systems: the skeletal structure, the musculature, and the linkages between them. The growing child should be encouraged to maintain erect posture without tension and strain. Flexibility, agility and correct posture are very important benefits for young bodies.

Control systems: for example, the nervous system and the endocrine system. The pineal is a tiny gland, located in the medulla oblongata of the brain. In yoga, it is closely linked with *ajna chakra,* the seat of wisdom and intuition. When the child is about eight years of age, the pineal begins to degenerate. This decay corresponds to the beginning of sexual maturation, precipitated by the release of hormones from the pituitary gland.

Many children do not cope well during this transitional period, when sexual awareness is developing. The high levels of these disturbing hormones in their blood cause an imbalance between their mental and vital fields. 'Vital' means *prana*, the bioenergy, and 'mental' means mind. The pranic and mental fields are unable to coordinate with each other and the glands such as the thyroid and adrenals do not work in absolute coordination with each other. Therefore, disruptive behaviour is often evinced at this age, such as anger, resentment or violence, much of which can be directly or indirectly attributed to hormonal imbalance.

Why burden a child with sexual responsibility at such a tender age? If we can find a way to delay the decay of the pineal gland, to maintain a balance between the sympathetic (*pingala*) and the parasympathetic (*ida*) nervous systems, then the child can continue to experience childhood without the stress of inappropriate impulses.

Metabolic systems: for example, the digestive system and the respiratory system. Since the physiological development of the lungs continues to take place up to the age of eight, it is important that children are encouraged to practise many forms of breathing techniques. Nadi shodhana, alternate nostril breathing, to balance the two hemispheres of the brain, or yogic pranayama, abdominal breathing, are two important examples for achieving efficiency in respiration with little energy drain. Children who swim find breathing exercises help them to swim longer under water. They learn how to utilize their full lung capacity.

Emotional/behavioural aspect

This aspect includes hyperactive behaviour, the phenomenon of relaxation and the culture of emotions. In yogic terminology, emotional disturbance is the result of an imbalance of *manas shakti* (the mental component) and *prana shakti* (the vital component). Where there is excess mental energy and a lack of prana, the child suffers withdrawal, depression, anxiety or lethargy. He lacks dynamism and cannot transform his mental energy into creative action. Conversely, if the child has excess prana and not enough manas, then he will become very destructive and disruptive. A vast amount of energy with no control spells disaster. It is comparable to a fast moving vehicle without brakes. Such hyperactive children are difficult to live with, and learning is almost impossible for them in this state.

Yoga automatically brings sobriety. Character and sobriety are expressions of inner purity, which cannot be infused solely by speeches. The practices must be performed.

Mental aspect

This includes the ability to concentrate, remember, reason, involving the conscious, subconscious and unconscious mind, and systematic stimulation of both brain hemispheres.

The new look in education had its preview back in May 1978 when the California State University held a conference for educators, educational consultants, counsellors, school and clinical psychologists, teachers and administrators. Workshops were devoted to metaphoric thought, biofeedback, T'ai Chi Chuan, meditation, guided imagery, dreams, psychotherapy, and psychic development in children. The term 'transpersonal psychology' was used to cover a broad range of positive inner experience and scientific validation. Teachers need to somehow enlarge their responsibilities to deal with the metaphorical and metaphysical, the aesthetic and dramatic, the spiritual and inspirational. They have dwelt too long on the safe ground of lectures, textbooks, tests and grades.

When we have children we want them to grow, therefore, if we are educators and yogis, we should keep in mind the goal of all these parental and educational cares. Where are we going? That idea is lacking nowadays in normal educational systems. There are techniques but there is no aim. We do not know what a human being can become. We think he or she amounts to being a professional, that he or she is going to be an acrobat or a teacher or a doctor or a carpenter or a good for nothing, but we do not perceive a higher purpose apart from that.

Creative aspect

This aspect includes imagination, visualization, vocalization and cultivation of one's own personality (as in the use of a resolve in yoga nidra). Children who begin asanas at a very young age can often be observed experimenting how to move from one posture to another in a type of dance. Children who have practised inner visualization often say that they look at a word and make an inner picture in order to learn to spell and recognize it while reading.

The system of yoga is designed so as to be applicable to any individual no matter what the age, level of interest, abilities or disabilities might be. Of course the potential for development is much greater if the practice of yoga is introduced as early as practicable and applied to individuals who do not suffer from disabilities.

Suitability of yoga for children

The practices of yoga not only help to keep the young body strong and supple but also incorporate mental activities, disciplines that help to develop attention and concentration, and stimulate the creative abilities that are latent within the child. Imagination in children under six is usually expended on toys and fairy tales, but we can also give them real things to imagine, putting them in a more accurate relationship with their environment, making them capable of dealing with this real world. The young child is more intuitive and less conditioned than an adult and is therefore quite open, forthright, creative and, above all, capable of learning. Yoga physiology suggests this is because the pineal gland has not started to degenerate due to calcification and that yoga practices aid in the delay of this degeneration. As the child grows older and enters school, these same yoga practices augment his learning abilities at school, and the regular discipline helps the growing child to channel and direct his emotional energies in a constructive manner.

Need for physical education

Professor Hans Kraus, former physician to J.F. Kennedy, insists that our inactive and overindulgent way of life is particularly dangerous for children who should be building up strong and supple muscles for their adult years. Physically gifted children or those naturally inclined to sports do not suffer as greatly as those who do not take to sports naturally, but even these children need encouragement to develop correct posture. For example, at the first session of a six week course for playground leaders, they were asked whether their own four to six year old children were able to bend forward and touch their toes without bending their knees. They all answered, "Of course, they are always running about." However, to their amazement, they found their children were unable to do this. So, running, climbing, riding, sliding do not necessarily result in a supple, flexible body. Prof. Kraus points out that some form of physical education is essential for all children. So why should children practise yoga and not some other physical exercises, like gymnastics or games?

Such other forms of physical activity are very good and should be introduced, but they are not suitable for all children. However, even children with physical disabilities can participate in yoga exercises because they are not just fast, energy burning, muscle hardening exercises. They are movements and postures for stretching and toning the muscles, for creating flexibility within the skeletal system, and they additionally affect the development and maintenance of healthy nervous and endocrinal systems.

Benefits for physically disabled children

Children who have suffered from polio and many other crippling disabilities have successfully practised yoga with great benefit. What is more important, their social development and their well-being benefits from the fact that they are able to participate in a class or session involving also the strongest and heartiest of children. This would be impossible under the conditions of gymnastics and games that presuppose normal health and require physical stamina or fast movements and competitiveness. Yoga is the answer for children who are in some way physically disabled to enjoy physical education without being set apart as different. Mentally disabled children can also benefit from yoga postures, kirtan, pranayama and karma yoga.

Yoga therapy for emotional disabilities

Emotionally disturbed, destructive, aggressive, hyperactive children can benefit from yogic discipline. The hyperactive child is restless, unable to concentrate or finish a job, overtalkative and a poor school performer. His troubles normally start at a very early age and are usually noticed by the mother before the child is two years of age. These children tend to have a history of feeding problems, disturbed sleep and poor general health in the first years of life. Many of these children have been disabled by delayed development of speech and poor coordination. As teenagers they tend to be more impatient, more resistant to discipline than their peers, and more prone to irritability and telling lies. A high proportion engage in fighting, stealing and deviant behaviour such as running away from home, going with a 'bad crowd' and playing truant; drinking is also not uncommon.

Amphetamines are being used to treat these hyperactive children. They act on the reticular formation, a key area in the brain stem at the top of the spinal cord, controlling consciousness and attention. Under their influence, the hyperactive child becomes quieter, exhibits a longer attention span, greater perseverance with assigned work and performs better at school. Amphetamines have a very similar effect on adults. They stimulate the release of noradrenalin, a neurotransmitter substance, from nerve endings and, therefore, in some way the normal balance of activity between noradrenalin and acetylcholine, another neurotransmitter, is brought about. However, the problem of drug treatment is that the effect of drugs is only temporary. When they wear off the child reverts to his usual behaviour. Additionally, drug treatment continued into adolescence leads to the danger of overuse and habituation.

In an article entitled, 'Charts of the Soul', in OMNI (1983), J. Hooper reported that F. Farley, an educational psychologist at the University of Wisconsin, suggests that hyperactivity and many learning difficulties are disorders of severe underarousal of the neural system. Other neurophysiologists are tracing the root of many of these related problems to a dopamine-acetylcholine imbalance; both neurotransmitters are necessary in the brain for transmission of impulses from one nerve cell to the other. Pranayama together with asanas works directly on the brain and the endocrinal system and, therefore, on the mind and emotional nature of the child, helping to re-establish emotional harmony and psychomotor normality, that is, normal attention span. We will illustrate the effect of yoga on hyperactive, aggressive children by recounting our experience and point out the need for a more accurate knowledge of the wide ranging effects of yoga practices.

A nine-year-old child was brought by his mother for yoga classes. She reported that he got up in the morning, beat his five year old brother before noisily going off to school where he also showed disruptive, aggressive behaviour. The only thing he seemed to enjoy was singing with the Vienna Boys Choir. At the end of the first yoga session he was told if he had enjoyed the class he should come back the following week; but if he did not want to come again he did not have to. He came back, with his mother's encouragement we are sure.

After a few sessions he was given his own practice, or sadhana, to be done every morning before breakfast. It consisted of surya namaskara, a series of twelve postures, and seven rounds each of simple alternate breathing in the nostrils, and bhramari pranayama, the humming bee breath.

Several months later his mother telephoned to say that if the director of the Vienna Boys Choir called, he should be told that her son was attending yoga classes on Thursday afternoons for the correction of a spinal problem. The class clashed with one of the choir practices on Thursday afternoons. She did not want him to stop either the yoga or the choir because he had become a much happier child at home. He did his yoga every morning then came quietly to breakfast before going to school.

When it was suggested that the director should be told that the boy was doing yoga to help correct an emotional problem, she insisted that he would not understand or accept that as a reason for attending a yoga class. This sadly reflects a common misconception that yoga is only a form of physical education and cannot form a basis of therapy for emotionally disturbed children as well. Yoga helps the child to channel his emotions and stimulates creativity in emotionally disabled children, which is not easily done with other forms of physical education.

Obviously, yoga is a form of complete education that can be used with all children because it develops physical stamina, emotional stability and intellectual and creative talents. It is a unified system for developing the balanced, total personality of the child.

Yoga and Education

1

The Need for a Yoga-Based Education System

Swami Satyananda Saraswati

It is little short of a miracle that modern methods of instruction have not already completely strangled the holy curiosity of enquiry, because what the delicate little plant needs most, apart from initial stimulation, is freedom; without that it is surely destroyed.

Albert Einstein

During the last twenty years I have tried to bring yoga into the homes and schools. There was a great misunderstanding about yoga when I was a child. It was thought that yoga was only for those people who were finished with life. If anybody was to practise yoga at a young age, people would remark, "Yoga, so early?" Even now, many people still think that yoga is only a pastime for retired people, but I always felt that yoga has more to do with the evolution of the human mind and the human body. Of course, as a child, it was not possible for me to understand yoga as well as I do now.

Preparing the mind

When you want to prepare a garden, grow flowers and trees, what do you do? Do you just sprinkle seeds? Many people might do that, but nothing would grow. First you have to prepare the soil, make it soft and pull out the weeds. Then you can sow the seeds and they will grow into nice flowers and fruit-bearing trees. The same law applies to the human mind. The mind has to be prepared for accepting the seeds.

The mind assumes many stages. There are certain stages where nothing goes into the head. Surely you have met such people in your life. Whatever you tell them falls on deaf ears; nothing penetrates their brain. They are like hard soil, and the best of seeds will not grow there, no matter how much you work at it. Then there are some people who are like soft soil. When you tell them something, they are completely responsive. These people have what are called receptive minds. Therefore, what is important in yoga is that we try to transform the quality of consciousness. Then everything can be planted in the mind without any obstruction.

Many years ago, when this became clear to me, I started to make various experiments with yoga. During my pilot projects, I tried yoga on many children. I would not say that I was one hundred percent successful, but through these experiments I came to certain conclusions about the influence of yoga on the evolution of the human mind.

Preserving the activity of the pineal gland

The first conclusion was concerned with a particular gland in the human body known as the pineal. This tiny gland, which is situated on the top of the spinal cord, has great importance. In fact, millions of years ago this gland played an active role in the development of the human brain. Therefore, people of those times had greater psychic and spiritual qualities and better control over their emotions, but with the passage of time the pineal gland has followed a course of degeneration. However, we find that today it is little more than a vestigial gland and if we do not take adequate measures to protect it, within a few thousand years it will be completely lost.

In yoga, the pineal gland is said to be the physical correlate of ajna chakra. Mystics and occultists refer to it as the third eye and philosophers call it the supermind. The pineal gland is very active in children, but by the time they reach the age of eight or ten it begins to calcify, and in elderly people it has little or no role to play in life.

This is very unfortunate because in yoga the pineal gland is considered to be the controlling and monitoring station in the brain. Just as an airport has a control tower, the human brain also has a directing, regulating and blocking tower, which controls all the faculties of the brain. In yoga we call this control station ajna chakra; the word 'ajna' itself means monitoring, ordering or regulating.

When the pineal gland starts to degenerate, the pituitary gland comes into action and the emotions shoot up. This is the reason why so many children become emotionally unbalanced and disturbed during their pre-adolescent and adolescent years. The pineal gland has a balancing influence on the activities of the brain, which keeps the whole brain in receptive order. Therefore, I found that those children in whom the pineal could still be commanded or monitored were much more receptive than those whose pineal gland was no longer active.

The second important point which I realized was that the adrenal glands have a very important role to play in the child's moral behaviour. Usually those with criminal tendencies have an overactive adrenal system. In terms of educating children, this has very important implications.

Stages of mental development in children

In the science of yoga, there are definite branches that control the functioning, behaviour and receptivity of the brain. Although the brain is a highly capable instrument of knowledge, this capacity sometimes undergoes periods of recession. In certain cases the brain is working very slowly. In others, the brain is evolved but dissipated.

Therefore, you will find that some children are dull in mind. Then again, some are very intelligent, but their thought patterns are dissipated. You will also find children who oscillate; at one moment they are very intelligent and the next moment they become like idiots. Then you will find another category of children who are very intelligent and consistent.

Dullness, dissipation, oscillation and one-pointedness are different stages in the evolution of the human brain. When children are intelligent and consistent, it is important to ensure that they do not regress. When children are sometimes intelligent and sometimes foolish, we must see that this oscillation stops. In those children who are very intelligent but dissipated, we must see that some kind of unification is brought into the patterns of their brain. Finally, we need to find a way of tuning or transforming the dull brain into an intelligent brain.

Yogic system of education

There are various processes through which knowledge can be implanted in the human brain. During the last few decades many methods have been introduced into the educational system. The oldest method, of course, is teaching in a classroom with a cane. When the child is intelligent give him a high mark, and when he is dull give him a big zero. The teacher gives a lecture, writes the points on a blackboard and the student is expected to understand. If he does not then give him a cross. This is a system of teaching, but not a system of education.

Real education is educating the behaviour of the mind and brain. There are other forms of teaching which have been introduced in the last few decades, but these too fall short of education. In most of these forms the actual learning process takes place only at an intellectual level. In the yogic system, however, the process of imbibing knowledge is a spontaneous affair which takes place at the deeper levels of the mind.

At every moment of our lives, right from birth, we are constantly receiving impressions, but these are not registered in the same form as when they went in. They are registered in the form of symbolic vibrations. Have the educators developed a system to teach children which works like this?

Geography, history, mathematics, physics, chemistry, biology, botany or anything can be taught through symbolic methods. This is the form of education which has to be used for the dull type of student. You can explain a certain concept to an intelligent child and he will understand it, but the dull child will not know what you are talking about because his conscious brain, his intellect, is incapable of receiving the knowledge that you are giving him. Therefore, you will have to transmit the knowledge in a symbolic form directly into his subconscious mind. This is precisely the system of education in yoga.

An experiment with yoga nidra

The principle of yoga nidra can be applied for increasing knowledge or developing the brain in dull boys and girls. Teachers and parents should be able to communicate with the subconscious mind of the child. This communication can take place only if you know how to develop the child's subconscious state.

I have tried many experiments with yoga nidra. For example, in 1964, a child of four came to join me as a swami. I could not accept him at such an early age, so I told him to come back when he was seven years-old and then I would accept him. To my amazement, on the day he turned seven, the boy left his home and came back to me. This gave me an indication of his mental character.

That boy lived with me for about eight years. Throughout this period he created unending problems and disturbances for me. All day long he used to break things and play tricks on the visitors who came to the ashram. He was not prepared to go to school or to study anything. So what did I do? I experimented on him with yoga nidra. As soon as he went to bed at night, I would note the time. Then after five minutes I would start reciting the Gita, the Upanishads, the Bible or anything else that I wanted him to learn. This worked very well so I did another experiment. I tried reading to him in English and then in other languages. I finished my experiment within two years and today he is one of the most brilliant swamis I have.

Physiological basis of yoga

The above indicates how the education of a child can be imparted even without the child's knowledge. The brain composition has to be influenced by certain practical methods. Through the practice of yoga nidra, pranayama, surya namaskara and chanting of mantra, the inner components of the brain can be brought to a point of regulation. Therefore, yoga should be properly investigated by educators.

Modern education cannot just bypass this truth by saying that yoga is a physical or gymnastic system, or that yoga is a science of the other world. Many scientific experiments have already been carried out. Yoga is not a system which should be regarded as being beyond the scope of scientific investigation.

The activities in the brain during the practice of pranayama have been investigated, and the claims of hatha yoga have been properly substantiated. Hatha yoga talks about ida and pingala nadis, the cold and hot channels. It states clearly that these two channels are physiological in nature. They are not abstract or symbolic, they are real. These two important channels exist within the framework of the spinal column. One channel controls the brain and its faculties of consciousness, and the other channel controls the life force and its impact on human existence. Therefore, these two channels should be properly regulated in order to ensure the balanced development of the child.

If there is a blockage in these two channels, the brain has to suffer. When a child is dull, how are you going to scientifically evolve this state of the brain? It is not enough to classify children as dull and forget about them. A dull brain can be tackled by rejuvenating the respective nadi or channel. When a child is found to be dull, it does not necessarily mean that he has some mechanical or structural defect in his brain. Dullness may be due to a deficiency in the quantum of energy supplied to the brain. Hatha yoga is very clear about this. It states that through the practice of pranayama, the pranas are extended to every part of the brain, increasing and awakening the total functioning capacity. Circulation of the pranas is very important, not only for physical activities, but also for mental activities.

With the help of pranayama, certain electrical activities are generated within the body. In scientific investigations, it has been shown that in pranayama the brain emits special electrical energies. In the same way, while practising yoga nidra one is not just sleeping. It has been noted that during yoga nidra, alpha waves are intensified. During ordinary sleep, however, delta waves are predominant. Whether one is sleeping soundly or is in the state of yoga nidra can be properly deduced by examining the brain activity recording for delta or alpha waves.

Hormonal block

Another important factor which has to be noted in educating the child's brain is that the blocks have to be removed from the hormonal structure. Sometimes the thyroid gland is not functioning properly and this can be the cause of mental dullness. Or perhaps the gonads are in a state of disharmony, which can also bring about dullness. Many children are very intelligent up to the age of 12 or 13, and then they suddenly drop back. This may occur particularly when the gonads are in a state of disharmony. The body assimilates a certain amount of hormones, then certain waste products are thrown out. When they are not properly eliminated they are reassimilated by the body, and that affects the functioning of the brain.

Freeing the minds of our children

The most important factor which we have to consider in regard to educating children is a very sad one. Children are not allowed to be free; they are restrained and controlled. They are pushed into modes of behaviour which are not natural to them. What happens is that we cast the shadow of our personality on the children. We have one image of ourselves, and our children have another. When children are small, they are helpless and have no choice but to accept our shadow within their mind, but when they grow up they revolt against it.

Actually, it is not the parents whom children revolt against. It is the structure which has been put into their minds. If there is useless furniture in your room you throw it out, not because you don't like the manufacturing of furniture but because it obstructs the room. Similarly, children don't want these impressions. They want to be free of them, to be able to think and act according to their own nature and choosing. After all, parents are also simple people. Not all are yogis, gurus or exemplary people. Parents fight because that is an emotional factor which cannot always be controlled. They are satisfied or dissatisfied with their children because that is the nature of parents, and because they don't know that this is going to affect the child's brain.

What can be done for children in this situation? Through the practice of antar mouna the impressions that are buried in the minds of children have to be eliminated. Children should be allowed to visualize, to fantasize, to operate their minds in absolute freedom, but first they must be made conscious of what is happening in their minds. They should not practise this independently, nor should they practise for a long period of time. They should practise this technique with your help and only for a short period. Then gradually, step by step, they will throw out the impressions they do not like or need.

Parents are very much in the minds of children, but it is necessary for the child's growth that the parents leave. As long as parents dominate the minds of children, they can never develop. Parental care can be an obstacle in the process of evolution of the child's brain. Of course, parents have to take care of their children; they cannot just throw them out or keep quiet and ignore them. However, there comes a time when a complete cleansing of the child's brain has to be done, and that can be accomplished through the practice of antar mouna.

Mantra and memory

The final point is the problem of memory. Memory is a great problem for children, i.e., the problem of encoding, storage and retrieval. All these processes combined are known as memory. Once you solve the problem of memory you solve the greatest problem in education. If you can find a method to improve the child's memory, you will be introducing something truly revolutionary into the educational system. People have tried different methods, but I have found that in order to develop the memory, children have to be guided through the path of mantra. The mantra works immediately on the subconscious and unconscious planes. With the help of mantra, antar mouna and yoga nidra a very clear memory can be developed in children.

How to implement yoga

Yoga should be properly introduced to children by educators. In my opinion, all the experiments that are being done in every part of the world in relation to the educational system should be compiled. A lot has been said and a lot is being done. Science is very clear about the effects of yoga on the brain and on human consciousness and character. The time has come to decide how to implement this as a practical scheme. Now it is up to educators to think about this project.

2

Yoga and Children's Problems

Swami Satyananda Saraswati

In India, children are traditionally introduced to the practice of yoga at the age of eight, nine or ten. The vedic tradition has a ceremony for children of this age in which they are taught surya namaskara, nadi shodhana pranayama and Gayatri mantra. This tradition still continues on a small scale today, but it is also necessary to include yoga in the formal educational system.

Children have many unexplained and unexpressed problems. They cannot express their problems correctly because their power of expression and their knowledge of their own psychology is not mature enough. Hence children usually express their problems through behaviour, and unless a psychoanalyst studies their behaviour he will not provide an accurate diagnosis.

Such problems become very difficult for most parents because they are not psychoanalysts and they consider the problems of their children subjectively. For instance, if a child is arrogant and disobedient, the parents will brand him as 'disobedient' but will not go deeper into the cause of the disobedience. If the child does not want to stay at home and would rather be with his friends, good or bad, the parents will brand him a vagabond or loafer. A psychoanalyst will try to analyze the cause, but most parents cannot do that. It is not that they don't know how to analyze, but just because they are the parents and are too biased.

There is an imbalance between certain tendencies in children from the ages of seven to twelve. Physical growth and psychological growth do not mature together. Sometimes, in relation to the brain, nervous system and endocrine system, physical growth is more advanced than mental growth and many times the mental growth is more advanced than the physical. This is the primary basis for problems in children.

We should not try to interpret the problems of children in the light of ethics and morality. For instance, if there is an excess of adrenal secretions, the child will be full of fears. He will not be able to face difficult people, and if he has a very serious teacher at school, he will not want to face the teacher and he will not like the subject either. The cause of the problem is not ethical or moral, or even social, it is psychophysiological. All we need to do is balance the adrenal secretions to change the character of the child. Those who are interested in working out the problems of children will have to study the emotional effects of the hormones in the system. Similar problems are also caused by an imbalance of the thyroid hormones.

At the age of seven or eight, the pineal gland starts regressing and when this process has advanced to a certain degree, the sex hormones start functioning in the body. Until this time, the pineal gland arrests the sexual consciousness in the child and also the associated rapid growth of the emotional and mental character. The moment the regression of the pineal gland is complete, the emotional growth becomes rapid and the child finds it difficult to adjust. If we can delay emotional growth in relation to physical growth, the child's stability is enhanced greatly. To do this we have to maintain the health of the pineal gland, and for this the practice of shambhavi mudra (concentration of the eyes at the eyebrow centre) is very important.

The pineal gland is very important. In yoga it is known as ajna chakra and it is situated in the brain at the top of the medulla oblongata. It is a very small gland and it acts like a lock. As long as the pineal gland is in good health, anarchical sexual behaviour does not occur. Sexual consciousness should develop when the child is able to balance his reaction in his mind. If awareness of sexual fantasies develops before he is able to express them, it can hit him hard. He may have frightening or confusing dreams, and try to overcome this awareness in his daily life. At the same time, in his day to day life, he tries to overcome this awareness by behaving in a way that people do not like. The early maturity of sexual awareness can thus almost break a child's mind. When the sex hormones start being secreted in girls for instance, the mammary glands, the ovaries and uterus all start to function. Now if the pineal gland is out of the picture too early, the whole confusion starts at the wrong time. The child becomes restless because she is not physically ready to express this new development.

Hence, it is beneficial for children to practise shambhavi mudra in order to influence ajna chakra inwardly and to delay sexual maturity until the correct time. To make this practice more interesting, we ask the child to visualize at the same time. We name about fifty items and let the child visualize them one by one. He keeps on moving his awareness, saying to himself and seeing, a pink rose, a flowing river, a snow-capped mountain, a moving car, an aeroplane in flight, a guava fruit, a church, and so on.

There are three ranges of objects to visualize: those which the child has seen, those he has not seen, and abstract concepts such as love/hatred. This practice not only helps the child to maintain psycho-emotional balance, it also develops his ability to visualize. Later on, when he is at school studying geography, history and mathematics, he will have a visualizing mind as well as a thinking mind.

Although we do not have strong scientific evidence I believe that other practices of yoga can also maintain the health of the pineal gland and add extra years to its life. This is why in India we have been teaching surya namaskara (a dynamic yoga exercise); nadi shodhana pranayama (for health and balance of the pineal gland); mantra (to challenge the child's distracted mind); and shambhavi mudra with visualization (to maintain the pineal gland).

3

Yoga with Pre-School Children

Arundhati

The child has his own laws of growth and if we want to help him grow we must follow him instead of imposing ourselves on him.

Maria Montessori

In 1968 Swami Satyananda Saraswati was asked which years were the most important in the life of a child. He replied that from about the fourth or fifth month of gestation to the end of the third year, when the child starts to develop reason, are most important. Since that time more sophisticated instruments have been developed for monitoring foetal development and neonatal responses, and scientific research carried out in USA and Scotland has validated this statement.

Swamiji also suggested that the emotions of the mother during pregnancy had an important effect on development. Watch a nervous mother on an aeroplane with baby and observe just how much her emotional state can affect the baby once it is outside the uterus. Sounds are audible to a foetus inside the amniotic sac which has caused scientists to ask if cognitive experiences actually begin before birth. The sound of Beethoven's Fifth Symphony being played by a mother half an hour before delivery was heard through a hydrophone inserted into her uterus. This caused one developmental psychologist to wonder just how a musical genius was born.

Imitative behaviour seems to be a natural reflex or instinct which is present within one hour of birth. Andrew Meltzoff, from the University of Washington studied the ability of neonates to imitate adults' facial gestures. Videotape recordings of close-ups of infants' faces showed that they stuck out their tongues more when the experimenters stuck out theirs, and opened their mouths when the experimenters did the same. Therefore, the best teaching method for children of this age would be for the parents themselves to practise yoga.

Cognitive development

Aside from Swami Satyananda's advice to study the ideas of Dr Montessori and to work with children, my yoga students, who were also parents of preschool age children, were instrumental in my starting to teach yoga to children of this age. They had found benefits from their own practice and wanted their children to have an advantage they had not had as small children: the opportunity to develop a supple, healthy physical body, as well as to stimulate creative thinking and intellectual growth. The life of the child cannot be cut in two, moving the limbs by sport and the mind by reading. Life must be one whole, especially at an early age when the child is constructing himself/herself, and yoga caters for the whole child.

During the first few years of life enormous physical development is accompanied by a still greater mental development. Mental development at this stage is a process of awakening. The child's innate curiosity is continually aroused by outside stimuli, and the brain is increasing in size and neural connections. Early childhood is the period in which numerous forms of self-control begin to develop, and the emergence of some capacity for voluntary self-control is clearly one of the most central and significant.

Vygotsky, a well-known Russian developmental psychologist suggests: "Cognitive development consists partly of the gradual transfer of control from others to the self, and the advent of these new abilities creates a transformation in the life of the child and those who interact with him because he becomes increasingly teachable and increasingly trainable." The development of language, communication, more accurate perceptions and logical reasoning are all taking place during this time of the child's life and he/she can readily respond to yoga.

In his article, 'Living with Children', published in the *Observer Magazine*, 1974, B. Jackson, Director of the Child Minding Research Development Unit suggests that in our society we "crudely underestimate the mind-dizzying potentialities of our children". He argues: "Our slowness in starting the educational process and the narrow interpretation of education that prevails, slows down enormously the increase in human talent. By the age of three a child is mastering the most complex skill it will ever acquire in life – speech. By the age of five the brain is already 90 percent of its adult weight. These are just two examples, but so much is already won or lost before the child glimpses school."

The importance of this period of life for learning is stressed by other very influential workers in the area of developmental psychology. Dr T. Bower, well-known for his research with young children at Edinburgh University, states, "The newborn infant can learn better than he ever will again". Dr Montessori (1948) in her book, *The Formation of Man,* also argues that when the child enters school at six he should already have the basic tools for education, namely reading and writing, well within his grasp. She writes: "Written language can be acquired much more easily by children of four years than by those of six years of age – the time at which compulsory education usually starts. While children of six years of age need at least two years to learn how to write, and do so with much difficulty and against nature, children of four years learn this second language (spoken being the first) within a few months."

She rightly argues that compulsory education, which begins with illiterate children of six, imposes upon them a rigid mental effort which breeds a certain disgust towards study and all intellectual instruction. It takes away their appetite for knowledge before they even begin to nourish themselves with it. One hears echoes of this same criticism of our educational system from M. Donaldson (1972) in her excellent book *Children's Minds,* when she questions why our educational system fails so many youngsters who were eager, enquiring preschool toddlers. Maybe it is the educators' insistence on imposing their ideas on the child rather than following the child's natural laws of growth and unfoldment. According to many scholars of child development, preschool age is the ideal time to start instilling discipline and stimulating creativity. These two very important aspects in the personality of the child are well developed through yogic practices.

Presenting yoga to pre-school children

How do we present yoga to children who are between two and six years of age? The yoga experience for the child of this age should not come through lessons but through play. L.S. Vygotsky (1933) suggests that play is not the predominant form of activity of the child but is, in a certain sense, the leading source of development in the preschool years. Play is purposeful activity for a child. Play for children in the early 'primitive' cultures always entailed doing what the parents did in real life. For example, in the Cheyenne tribe of the American midwest, young boys made play bows and arrows and pretended to hunt as a game. This play was, of course, preparing the child for his forthcoming duties as an adult within the society. In play a child creates an imaginary situation and this fact can be regarded as a means of developing abstract thought.

Imagination is a new formation in the preschool child which is not present in the consciousness of the very young child; it is totally absent in animals and represents a specifically human form of conscious activity. In play, activity is separated from objects, and action arises from ideas rather than from things. Action in the imaginative sphere, in an imaginary situation, the creation of voluntary intentions and the formation of real life plans and volitional motives, all appear in play and make it the highest level of preschool development. At school, play does not die away but permeates the attitude to reality. It has its own inner continuation in school instructions.

People do not learn by being taught but learn by experiencing the consequences of their actions. It has been found that learning through playing games has a number of intrinsic virtues, one of these being their attention-focusing quality. Games tend to focus attention more effectively than most other teaching devices, partly because they involve the student actively rather than passively. Play and games are a very old and widespread form of learning, and with the results of the plentiful research on play, it is being adopted in the form of games for use with older children and teenagers, not just preschool children. Role playing is widely used with children and teenagers living in correctional homes, or institutions or schools. It is used as a form of emotional and behavioural therapy, a way to learn social skills.

In studies of the role of play in problem solving by preschool children, Sylva, et al (1974) found that those who were allowed to play with the experimental equipment before attempting problem solving did better for the following reasons:

1. Solving problems required self-initiation and the playing children were the only ones in the study who demonstrated self-initiation.
2. Tool invention (the problem to be solved) requires serial ordering of the constituent acts involved.
3. Play reduces the stress of anticipating success and failure. Therefore, these children could benefit from hints and could approach the solution gradually without breaking off. But play and games must be presented in different ways, according to the age of the children involved.

According to Dr Montessori (1948) it is clear that play has an important bearing on the development of the child.

One of the characteristics of play which she pointed out is, "that after choosing some activity in the form of play the child repeats it over and over again". It has long been known that infants and children spontaneously 'practise' each new skill as it arises. Therefore, when doing yoga with children of this age one can easily repeat the same class many times, since the child himself will often request to do what he did before. Anyone who has worked in playgroups will know how often a favourite story must be read and re-read, at least two or three times at the child's request during each storytime. Or, if it is a game or a dance where parts are taken by the children, young children want to play each part so it has to be done again and again.

So, presenting yoga to the preschool child must be done through play. However, the teacher must remember that behind the actuality of play there has to be a clear-headed theory of learning, a sense of how a mind and a personality might grow, and a reasonable range of targets. As Dr Montessori writes: "...the attempts of so-called modern education which simply tries to deliver the child from presumed repression are not on the right path. To let the pupils do what they like, to amuse them with light occupations, to lead them back to an almost wild state, does not solve the problem."

B. Jackson argues this same point as well, saying that "one must know where one is going and why, or one is simply entertaining children". While enjoying the play with the children, the yoga teacher does not want to simply entertain but to provide an environment for utilization of all yoga activities for unfolding and balancing the total personality of the child. As the child grows older and enters school, the presentation of yoga can take on a more structured form as do other class activities.

4

Yoga Lessons Begin at Age Eight

Dr Swami Karmananda Saraswati

In India, children traditionally receive their initial yoga instructions at the time of *upanayanvidhi*, the thread ceremony, in the eight year. In the ancient culture, boys and girls alike were initiated into surya namaskara, nadi shodhana pranayama and Gayatri mantra at this magical age which represents 'childhood's end'. Now the significance of this age is becoming apparent to modern scientists, who recognize that the eighth year of life represents a crucial milestone in the physiological and psychological development of each individual, marking the beginning of the transition of awareness from childhood into adult life. The following are a number of facts which have been discovered by scientists concerning children of this age.

- The number of minute alveoli (air sacs) in the lungs goes on increasing until the eighth year. After this age the alveoli increase in size only, there being no further duplication of alveoli occurring. Doctors note that this is the ideal age for the introduction of pranayama into the daily routine. In this way the cardiovascular and respiratory mechanisms will be trained systematically, ensuring vitality and high levels of resistance and endurance throughout the different stages of life.
- The development and programming of the immune surveillance system which proliferates rapidly during intra-uterine life, infancy and early childhood, ceases at this

age when the lymphoid tissues of the thymus gland, lying wrapped around the base of the heart and the root of the lungs, begin to wither and atrophy. The nature and sensitivity of immune responses mounted by the individual later in life are thus virtually determined by the eighth year. The psychological and physiological process of differentiation between 'self'and 'other', which in spiritual life manifests as the formidable, yet illusory, barrier of the 'ego', is also responsible at a cellular level for immune deficiency diseases such as asthma, allergic reactions, arthritis, tumours and cancers. Yogic practices of surya namaskara and nadi shodhana pranayama ensure continual and ongoing development of the immune responses throughout life so that the yogi can continually mount appropriate responses to each new situation and set of circumstances in life. This ensures that he will always respond in a healthy adaptive way to all sets of conditions rather than responding according to the fixed 'cellular' record encoded up to the eighth year, when development of the immune memory ceases in the average person. This inability to integrate later life circumstances and situations with the pre-existing cellular memory is one cause of the immune deficiency and hypersensitivity diseases which are so rampant in modern societies.

- The pineal gland, which has a controlling influence over the pituitary and the whole endocrine system, begins to decay in the eighth year. This tiny structure in the centre of the brain is responsible for maintenance of the child's expanded state of awareness, devoid of sexual consciousness and role. After eight years, the powerful pituitary reproductive hormones are gradually unleashed, and the onset of puberty results as pineal decay continues. Children who commence yoga practices in the eighth year experience a delay in pubescence, maintaining the childlike state for several more years. The awakening of adult emotional and sexual impulses and passions is thus postponed until the individual is ready to cope with the emotional, psychological and physiological revolution which heralds the adoption of male or female social and sexual identity. Children in whom puberty and menarche occur later have been found to be generally more intuitive, intelligent and sensitive adults than the early maturers who are forced to confront the conflicts and emotional turmoils of adult life before they are capable of managing and understanding what is occurring within their bodies and minds.

- According to psychologists, the child's abstract reasoning capacities, the ability to understand concepts and ideas which form the basis of ongoing technical and moral education, begins from the age of eight years. This is the time when a child can be considered ready to learn and to concentrate seriously. Before age eight, play and fantasy constitute the child's world, but after this turning point, discipline and concentration should be gradually introduced to the child. Children who practise yoga from this age are destined to expand and develop their natural attributes, capacities and talents to the fullest extent, leading successful, useful and liberating lives.

From the age of eight, children should be educated in an international cultural atmosphere. It is not books, prayers, church or temple which should become the basis of the spiritual culture. The spiritual education of a child should begin with self-culture. Whether he lives in an ashram, monastery, hostel, or at home with his parents, a child should be given the opportunity to participate in day-to-day work. Work along the lines of karma yoga is the best way of inculcating spiritual experiences and spiritual samskaras. As Swami Satyananda Saraswati has said: "The destiny of the whole world depends on the little children. If you want to see the silver lining on the horizon it is not you and me, but the children who have to be spiritualized."

5

Student Unrest and Its Remedy

Swami Satyananda Saraswati

We are passing through a period of general unrest. Whoever you meet and talk with will express dissatisfaction with the existing conditions of life. Contemporary man appears to be incapable of adjusting to circumstances, nor does he know the purpose of his life. There is no mission or object to his life and he has no philosophy of life. He is afraid of others and considers himself to be a victim of circumstances. He is at breaking point every moment. Under such circumstances spontaneous outbursts of wild anger are natural. Our students are no exception to this phenomena. There are other inherent causes for the manifestation of violent animal instincts in our young people which make them become enemies of peace. We call it student unrest.

There are people who do not attempt to go to the root of the problem but who conveniently link the issue with the social, political or economic problems of the country. Some blame our systems of education and suggest a change without, however, giving any concrete or definite solutions. Our system of education has already undergone various experiments and the remedies have proved to be worse than the disease. It is high time that the education experts sat together, worked out a diagnosis and then prescribed effective remedies for the ailments.

Our modern educational institutions have ceased to play their role effectively. They are nothing more than factories

which produce money-making machines. Whe
go out of order, they are apt to create problems.

With the growth of modern science and techn
demands of society are constantly changing. A g
people trained for a particular trade today may be unfit and useless for a new industry tomorrow. The round pegs prepared by our educational institutions will not fit in the square holes. The result is unemployment and the populace becomes panicky.

Money-makers or divine creators

Even parents look at their children in terms of money. This is really painful. They should think that their wards are a spark of the divine soul, a being which has come from somewhere, and that they are only trustees of that soul as it undergoes the process of unfoldment. Contemporary methods of education allow a parent to give all the necessary comforts of life to his child, but what he gets in return is, at best, a degree-holder and egoist, a beautifully polished but undisciplined animal. Out of a hundred boys entrusted to the temples of learning, sixty of them are returned as outlaws. This brings to mind the statement that "the medical operation was a success but unfortunately the patient died". The big universities, palatial institutions, pregnant libraries and great centres of learning may fulfil other purposes, but not the one for which they were instituted, if they fail to develop the real dignity in man.

Ideal education should be based on something more than commercial implications. Individuals in the world today are eagerly striving for unity within themselves and with others. They are sick and tired of the treasure-oriented life of man, but the structure of present-day life does not aid or facilitate outlets for the innermost urges of mankind.

The wrong concept of individual self-expression has done immeasurable harm to society as a whole. Sometimes ignorance is preferable to wrong or perverted knowledge. The modern educator's concept of individual self-expression is based on the body-mind complex. But there is also the changeless, eternal, ever perfect substance, the soul, to be considered. There are needs for restraint of the personality on the one hand and for unfoldment of the being on the other.

We see an ascending pattern everywhere in nature, a progressive evolutionary movement from the mineral to the vegetable world, an upward trend which is said to culminate in man. Man, considering himself thus to be the supreme peak, fails to think of any other further possible evolution and begins busying himself with external objects only. He tries to capture nature for his personal ends. This is very sad. He forgets to realize that he still has a long way to climb, that he is still unfinished material. This stage is only the beginning of true evolution. The door to higher evolution is only opened when he acquires this body. Until now he has reached the level of man through involuntary processes. He must act purposefully towards a definite end. Human evolution is only just beginning. Education should illuminate the inner genius already in man and help in the process of evolution. It should develop an integrated and balanced personality in man and aid towards making man divine.

It appears that there is something wrong somewhere in the system of our education which blocks the way of achieving the very purpose for which it was instituted. If the present-day unrest were visible only in India, one might reasonably link it with social, political or economic conditions. The pattern of unrest in India may be different but the result is the same as elsewhere throughout the world. We have already seen what has happened in France, West Germany, USA, Japan, in the presidential dictatorship of Pakistan, and even in a country like Sweden where there are practically no problems at all. On the slightest provocation, students in these countries stormed public and private buildings. In Sweden, students destroyed government and private property, just for the excitement or only out of curiosity. Why this need for excitement? Is it not the result of an unbalanced personality?

Evolving the whole brain

Apart from the obvious deficiencies in the methods of our education and the faults inherent in our educational attitudes, we cannot continue to ignore the silent changes that are going on in the very structure of the human mind. This is no less a cause for what is happening in society and our young people are wrongly blamed for that. We must have a reasonable approach to the problem in order to come to a right conclusion.

To my mind, the problem is more a psychophysiological or biochemical one than anything else. In the evolution of mankind the grey matter of the brain constantly changes and the vast development of man's intellect agitates the centre of sensibility in his mind.

This change has been more effectively and speedily going on among young people between the ages of eighteen and thirty and is discernible in their temperaments, their actions and their behaviour. They destroy even the most beautiful art gallery of antiquity on the slightest provocation. Going to church or to a temple is a sign of hypocrisy to them. They question the very existence of God, without knowing the meaning of supreme consciousness, the theory of relativity or scientists' efforts to jump beyond the mind. They are highly conscious of their rights but forget to think of their duties. These young people have lost their capacity for true discrimination.

When man loses his capacity for discrimination, when a particular nerve centre in his head which is responsible for his behaviour becomes agitated, no amount of preaching or intellectual injunction can possibly constrain him. At that particular moment, what is required is a purely scientific approach, since philosophy and religion have their limitations. For centuries past we have been preaching our rich philosophy, but it has failed to attain the desired objectives. Now the time has come when we should adopt quite different attitudes based on the experiments and results of scientific research.

Yoga as the philosopher's stone

Our ancient system of hatha yoga is an answer. It purifies the body. Pranayama and mudras silence the agitated centres of the mind and adjust faulty endocrine secretions. The practices automatically bring sobriety. Character and sobriety are the expressions of the inner purity of mankind. These cannot be infused from outside solely by speeches. The practices must be performed.

In Australia, where the problem of unrest among young people has become acute, some successful experiments were made with yoga. Pranayama was introduced in order to allay the restless minds of the young. It has the capacity to influence the nerves, glands and other physical functions of man. It can correct wrong behaviour, reset erroneous mental patterns and change attitudes towards other people and surroundings.

The mental condition of the human mind plays a very important role in the appreciation of material set before an individual and in his adjustment to circumstances. If we really want to curb the growing unrest among our young people, we will have to become aware of the agitated cerebral centres and control them in such a way that the students themselves will hate the attitude which causes agitation. The students themselves must be trained to become aware that they can perform reasonable actions for which they will be willing to accept responsibility.

Educators in turn must answer their own responsibility towards the students by actively guiding them with reliable and effective methods.

6

Yoga and the Youth Problem

Swami Satyananda Saraswati

Is everything wrong with our younger generation, and is there no way of redemption for today's youth other than the law and social welfare schemes? An ideal educational syllabus evolved by the ancient Indian culture included a process of 'auto-mental' education, which was successfully taught to and practised by students for centuries. Today, after a lapse of a few hundred years, it is claimed that the content of the ancient life-moulding system has been rediscovered and will revitalize future generations all over the world. The basis of this much acclaimed system is yoga.

Young people today are seeking to break down the barriers of society, to create a new means of expression, to improve society and rectify the injustices which they see around them. In this respect they are no different to young people throughout the history of mankind; they have always sought to change the existing order, whether in their parent's house, in their village, in their town or in their country. What is different in the present modern age is that because of the advent of international communication, young people are able to know the ideas of other young people in other countries, share ideas and widely publicize new means of expression or decry injustices internationally. It is a natural process in nature for young people to 'rebel' against tradition, for without it man would not evolve. By not accepting tradition, young people are only trying to find a place in life where they can be happy, a place in accordance with their individual nature and not in opposition to their nature.

Popularity of yoga among young people

Today a strange thing is happening. Whilst young people have rejected most old ideas, even ideas that were popular only ten years ago, they have flocked in large numbers to the ancient tradition of yoga. The number of people who practise yoga is increasing in all age groups, but young people in particular are attracted to yoga. Why is this? Why have young people throughout the world started to adopt yoga as their way of life? Older people should consider this phenomenon carefully, for every major change that has occurred in the history of mankind has occurred through youthful dissatisfaction that has continued into adult life, where the individual or individuals have effected change. So it seems more than a probability that the interest young people show in yoga will infiltrate the whole of society.

It is a common cry among the older generation that young people have too much freedom and use their time pursuing useless things. They show a great interest in all kinds of music which is incomprehensible or even nauseating to older people. They wear unusual clothes, which seem most strange to their elders. They indulge in drugs which older people object to and condemn. The fact that their critics consume large amounts of alcohol is conveniently forgotten, and so on. Actually it can be said in all sincerity, whether these criticisms are valid or not, that young people of today are the most 'truth-orientated' group of people that have ever existed. Whatever young people do, good or bad in the eyes of their mothers and fathers, they have, as no other generation has dared to, removed and discarded taboos, tradition, restrictions and hypocrisies on an unprecedented scale. The circumstances in the world make it possible. Modern technology and widespread education have given young people more facilities and the chance to 'do their own thing'. The very fact that young people are experimenting with so many different things is actually a positive contribution to the evolution of mankind. Older people should watch them and learn from them.

It is in the search for truth that young people have universally adopted yoga. They have discovered that yoga does not ask them to accept dogmas or stereotyped ideas. It merely suggests techniques and then tells people to find out things for themselves. Yoga gives them a way of life that transcends national boundaries, something that people throughout history and large numbers of people today cannot understand. If I am an Indian then I must love India more than any other country. If I am English then England must be the greatest country, and so on. Of course, most people never question the sense in this kind of thinking. The young person of today, however, is too wise; he knows this is not the truth and that it is just blind dogma and the cause of futile wars throughout the ages. Yoga has started to flourish again after thousands of years of sleep because the wisdom of present-day young people demands it. If yoga in any way preached dogma, untruths or slogans against their fellows, young people would not even try it, let alone adopt it as they have. If yoga had said, "This is the only way to live your life and other systems are completely wrong", young people would not have been attracted to it.

Today, more than any other time in history, there is a crisis in status. Few people are sure of their place in time and space, in the world, in their country, in their work or in their homes. This is the case with old and young people alike. There are so many conflicting ideas and possibilities open to most people, and when there are so many different things that each person can do with their life, they become confused and do not know which direction to take. How much easier it was in the old days when each person followed in his parents' footsteps and knew what he would be doing, not only tomorrow but in twenty years time also.

So what can young people do; how can they decide what the basis for living their life should be? They can ask their parents, but they know instinctively that their parents are as they are. They want happiness and contentment, and these things few of their elders know about, for as one great writer put it, "most people lead lives of quiet desperation". Can anyone expect young people to follow their parents when they see that underneath all the show and pomp their parents are really unhappy in the lifestyle that they lead? They see that their elders' way of life gives happiness only on fleeting occasions, perhaps when they unexpectedly earn a lot of money or when they go to the cinema or when they eat some very nice food. Young people perceive and rightly so, that everyone's life should be a continual expression of joy.

Yoga: the path to happiness

Happiness is the true condition of man. This is why the younger generation has taken to yoga; to find their true nature and so find permanent happiness that transcends the transitory happiness given by sensual pleasures and so on. In yoga they can see a complete way of life which tackles all the facets of man's being. They see that the techniques of asanas and pranayama give physical and mental health, the most basic step to achieving permanent happiness. How very different this is from the older generation who tend not to worry very much about this aspect of their being; if their bodies work, all is well, even if they have pain, indigestion and so on, through misuse. Young people have positive attitudes about health; they do not wait for illness to occur, but prevent it occurring. They realize that maintaining or obtaining good mental health is the next step to permanent happiness. Older people do not seem to give much consideration to this factor in their lives even though they feel continually tense; and if they do give this factor consideration it is because they have been stricken by grave mental problems.

Again it is the younger generation who are leading all on to a positive path to mental peace, for all over the world they have adopted meditation and other yogic practices as being a necessary part of the daily routine. And what about the spiritual side of life? Whilst older people have accepted religious ideas handed down through the ages without really understanding their basis, or have even rejected religion as being 'rubbish' as seems to be the modern trend, young people have again taken the initiative. They have started to try and 'experience' the truths inherent in all religions. They have not accepted, nor have they rejected religions. They have, in fact, adopted a more scientific approach by trying to find the truth through practical methods. In this endeavour they have taken to the yogic techniques.

I once talked to a young man of eighteen who told me he did not feel he could see his place in society. His parents had already disowned him because of his rebellious nature. He told me that he did many 'crazy' things with his friends for no other reason than that he could not see why he shouldn't do them. He told me that he was looking for something, though he did not know what. All his actions were in an attempt to express some inner feeling. He felt there was a permanent, universal correct action for each individual but could not find out what it was. He looked around him and saw hypocrisy, people were not doing what their nature dictated, their dharma, but were doing things in life that did not come from their inner being; doing things automatically like a machine because their neighbours expected them to do a particular action.

He felt that people were continually suppressed because they were continually "acting their lives to impress the people around them". It was as a reaction to the way of life that most people lived, that he had done 'crazy things', as he put it. He said that he had heard that yoga was a method of knowing the inner nature and so attaining happiness. Was it true? I told him it was perfectly true. I told him that as he wanted to know more, and to practise yoga, he should go to a yoga school, the address of which I later gave him. I met that same person six months later. I didn't ask him if he had been doing yoga, I could see by his face. He told me that yoga had changed his whole life. At last he had found the way to permanent happiness in life and now he knew, in a small way at the present, that there was one truth underlying everything that was devoid of hypocrisy and superficiality. He was now on good terms with his parents and was trying to convince them to think about their attitude to life, and to persuade them to do yoga.

Positive evolution

Imagine what would happen if yoga were taught in every school in the world, just as we teach mathematics or science. When we consider that about sixty percent of the world's population are children, the implications are staggering. Young people everywhere would be well-adjusted, healthy and happy. Perceptive and understanding, physically and mentally fit, they would be aware of their own potential and more capable of its realization. With their spiritual experience they would be able to operate on a different and higher level of consciousness, and this could be brought to use in the outer life, in their work and social pursuits. Yoga encourages service, and this could be utilized for the greater benefit of mankind. With yoga in the curriculum of universities and colleges, a better graduate would be produced who would be more perceptive in applying his intelligence to his work.

Everyone should invest in yoga, young and old. The future of young people and the world needs a system such as yoga. Yoga means 'union' and that is just what we could achieve – a union of people throughout the world. By yoga everyone would gain insight into their own culture and their own way of life to a level never before believed possible. Such is the power of yoga. It is not a religion, but a science of living according to our means and to the laws of life. If we hold ourselves responsible for the future, our own and our children's, then we will ensure that the evolution of man is along positive lines. Only then will wars cease; only then will man be able to love his fellows, and only then will adults understand the young, and the young understand the old.

7

Better Ways of Education

Dr Swami Shankardevananda Saraswati

The search for new and improved methods of education continues, as it has done through the ages. With the discovery and application of yoga, it seems as though a breakthrough is about to take place. The scientific discovery of the functions of the different sides of the brain has furthered the cause of yoga and expansion of consciousness by explaining the need for the implementation of these disciplines in our lives.

The brain is divided into two cerebral hemispheres. Each hemisphere appears to have a separate and quite different function. The right hemisphere is associated with the intuitive and spatial aspects of our being, while the left is associated with the analytical and linear capacities. Up to now, education has mainly focused on the left hemisphere, giving importance to linear, scientific and purely logical disciplines such as reading, writing and arithmetic. The artistic, intuitive and less quantitative subjects, such as art, dance and other creative activities, have received negligible support, both financially and in school programs. Educators are showing us that this approach is lopsided and will lead to partial education and even deleterious effects in our lives.

According to Jerry Smith, an education professor at Indiana University, USA, teachers have lost touch with the mystery of their calling because of narrowly defined education rituals. The present syllabuses are too rigid. They do not fulfil us as human beings or satisfy the basic needs we are all searching for in life.

A special issue of the university's School of Education Bulletin states: "Teachers must somehow enlarge their responsibilities to deal with the metaphorical and metaphysical, the aesthetic and dramatic, the spiritual and inspirational. We teachers have dwelt too long on the safe ground of lectures, textbooks, tests and grades."

Educating the whole brain

Education researcher Vivian Sherman has warned of a strong, silent stumbling block to the union of the intellectual and intuitive (the left and right sides of the brain) in the present education system. Sherman states that left brain schooling (purely intellectual training) is modelled on an incorrect and inaccurate concept of science. Most of the great scientific discoveries, such as those of Newton and Einstein, were precipitated by flashes of intuition, cosmic insight into the nature of the whole, and understanding of the relationships underlying the basis of the material universe. They were then carried to their logical and practical conclusions by the analytical process.

As a means of unifying the brain, researchers have been studying the effects of meditation, yoga asanas, pranayama, biofeedback, and so on. They are attempting to sort out what goes on in the brain and what we can do to affect the various processes. Some amazing results have emerged. Banquet, for example, has shown that in kriya yoga the whole brain is unified, acting as a single unit instead of the jumbled and chaotic mess that many people experience. Many said this was accompanied by a blissful and life-affirming experience. Many people report that after kriya yoga they are full of energy and in touch with the creative energy and knowledge of the cosmos. They begin to tap the knowledge within all of us which has resulted in many books and external forms of knowledge or information. This ability appears to emerge when both sides of the brain unify.

In yogic terminology, the unification of the two sides of the brain is called the awakening of sushumna nadi, the pranic channel which runs down the spinal cord. The left side of the brain, the logical and extroverted side, corresponds to pingala nadi, which runs down the right side of the body, and the right side of the brain corresponds to ida, the internal aspects of mind and formless energy. Basing their research on the already established science of yoga, many scientists are finding the explanations for their experimental evidence already existing in the ancient yoga shastras.

Yoga: the evolutionary catalyst

A new blueprint is being laid down for the union of meditation, science and education as a means of enlarging the scope of present educational techniques. The accelerated learning technique of Georgi Lozanov of Bulgaria utilizes the essentials of yoga nidra to allow information and knowledge to enter the brain and mind at deeper subconscious levels. Thus the intellectual process of learning is bypassed and made anachronistic. This subtle technique of learning is becoming increasingly popular worldwide. Don Schuster of Iowa State University reported that yoga nidra and suggestology type techniques used by Judy Tyler, an Atlanta third grade teacher, enabled remedial students to make up two years work in only one semester (approximately four months).

The new look in education had its preview in May 1978 when the California State University held a conference for educators, educational consultants, counsellors, school and clinical psychologists, teachers and administrators. Workshops were devoted to metaphoric thought, biofeedback, T'ai Chi Chuan, meditation, guided imagery, dreams, psychotherapy, and psychic development in children. The term 'transpersonal psychology' was used to cover the broad range of positive inner experience and its scientific validation.

The conference seems to point out that transcendental or mystical experience will be recognized as complementary to cognitive, psychomotor and effective learning in the near future by teachers and institutions. Meditation and how to get high naturally will be taught in school, not only to relax the body, mind and personality, but also to open the right side of the brain and allow us to reach new vistas of experience and knowledge. Education will be enriched thereby. Yoga will play a role by enabling students and teachers to follow systematic, safe and practical techniques which are ladders to higher awareness.

By expanding our intuitive nature, the practices of yoga help us towards synthesizing the various elements of our environment into a structural whole. The ability to view the total picture is enhanced. Thus the relationships and interrelating factors in the environment and inside ourselves are understood and woven into a pattern of thinking that helps us to further understand the world in a neverending cycle of growth.

The developed intuition helps us in learning the logical side also. School subjects can then be better understood when examined from the point of view of the visualizing mind. This theory has been demonstrated by the 'alternative' Magnet Arts Elementary School in Eugene, Oregon, USA, where reading and writing skills are taught via playwriting and acting. Dance is used in mathematics instruction and science students also learn how to make musical instruments. The school's sixth grade students tied for first place in reading, and fifth place in mathematics amongst the district's thirty schools.

By enhancing the crystallization of growing brains and developing minds; in developing practical ways to balance the dual aspects of our nature: brain and mind, inner and outer, left and right, intuitive and analytical; by providing worthy goals for young people, in order to avoid the disastrous consequences of an ill-managed identity crisis and to provide a positive direction in life, yoga is the means to a better education system from both the student's and the teacher's point of view.

Relaxation for school children

Since education is one of our first priorities when we think of ways of improving our society, then how do we decide what is the best thing to teach and the best way to teach it? Up till now most education has been concentrating on imparting professional skills and developing the intellectual side of our nature. However, there remains a big deficiency in education directed at making us better human beings. This has been left up to the parents and religious institutions, but given the state of the world today, there is still room for improvement.

The introduction of yogic techniques would go a long way towards filling this vacuum in our present educational systems. Not only would it help to make us better people, but by helping us to relax and concentrate, we would be able to learn our reading, writing and arithmetic. A research report by psychologist S.H. Harlem seems to substantiate this. Harlem used an adapted version of the yogic relaxation technique which stands at the base of today's biofeedback movement. Twenty-nine school children (average age seven years) were in the experimental group and were compared with thirty controls. The experiment consisted of training over ten days with ten minutes of daily relaxation. The controls were brought together informally for the same period of time.

Two weeks later a series of psychological tests for cognitive abilities and muscle tension was carried out. These showed that the experimental group had pronounced changes in all the measurements, improved awareness, concentration, memory and cognitive adaptation. The muscle tension readings, measured on an electromylograph, showed that they were more relaxed physically, implying a concomitant mental relaxation, and that they had been able to maintain this relaxation over a period of time.

The value of increased concentration and memory from an early age is easily appreciated by all who have finished the long road of schooling and the tortures of annual examinations. If only we had known this then.

8

Yoga at School

Swami Yogabhakti Saraswati

I am a teacher of English and I also teach yoga. For a long time I did both separately, that is, I taught English in my school and yoga outside in my ashram, but finally something happened. By learning and imbibing yoga, I found my way of teaching English had also improved in a subtle way. That was important but was not the only benefit.

I received an answer to the question I had asked myself at the beginning of my career as an English teacher. Is teaching the way I have been trained to teach really teaching, or is it putting the children out of shape? Finally, I found by changing myself I could teach in a way that was more satisfactory both to myself and the children. I started thinking about the teaching process and conducting experiments in my classroom. I started teaching yoga to children, but not in a hall. I do not give yoga sessions to children, I do not teach them yoga on Fridays or Wednesdays. I introduce yoga into the classroom so the children are stuck and cannot evade it.

Since I am a yoga teacher outside the classroom I am somehow stamped by it and so the children have an English teacher immersed in yoga; they cannot escape from it and they seem to enjoy it quite well. If they have me, they are bound to go through my method. So I have become known in France as a teacher who teaches English through yoga.

It all started in France when some journalists came to listen to a lecture given by Swami Satyananda Saraswati at

Condorcet, the High school where I was teaching. When they heard him advocating yoga for children so well, they said, "That's all right but can we see it?" It so happened that school was starting again after the holidays so they came into the classroom and saw what I was doing. That was in 1979 and since then numerous newspapers have publicized the experiment.

In France we are lucky to have a young Swiss man helping us, named Jacques de Coulon. He is a school teacher and has written a book on the subject of yoga for children. He introduced his pupils to the yoga exercises he learned at a Coptic school which he had visited while in the USA during a sabbatical leave. There he learned some exercises which can probably be traced to the time of the ancient Egyptians. After his return he wrote a thesis called 'The Awakening and Harmonizing of the Child's Personality'. The publisher heard about my experiments in Paris and wrote to me saying that he had edited a book which seemed to contain an account of experiences similar to the ones I had had with my experiments. I obtained the book, then met the author and we worked together organizing seminars.

Because of this theoretical background, together with the practice at College Condorcet in Paris, we have found recognition in France, and many teachers have managed to introduce our exercises into their own classrooms. The movement thus started, quickly gained momentum and I am going to explain why.

If you go to regular yoga classes you will find that a large proportion of the participants are teachers or educators. Why do so many people of the teaching profession practise yoga? Personally, I feel that in the course of time yoga will become more and more important due to the increase in teachers trying it. In France, as in England, Scotland, Ireland and all over the world, more and more teachers are practising yoga. The reason they are practising yoga is due to the loss of vitality entailed by their presence everyday in the classrooms.

Formerly, people worked very hard physically, cutting wood, carrying water, polishing floors by hand and so on. Now they do not work so hard, yet they get very tired. Teachers, generally, are not weary from doing physical labour, and they have a lot of holidays (that is their reputation) yet they are extremely tired. When the holidays come, teachers are really exhausted. They have realized that this weariness is not something that can be mended by just sleeping. There must be ways and means to recapture this energy which is dissipated through teaching. It is a very difficult job but nobody can see where the fatigue comes from. As a result of practising yoga, my energy level has increased. I realized that through yoga I might obtain what I needed to carry out my profession. I think a lot of teachers do yoga, as I did, because yoga will help them.

Yoga and classroom problems

What are the problems encountered by the teacher in the traditional classroom situation and how can yoga alleviate them?

- Firstly, the job is tiring because children need a lot of movement. When they are sitting in the classroom for three to six hours on end, they become very nervous and agitated, and they want to romp around and talk. So the teacher must say, "Keep quiet!" "Listen!" "Pay attention!" However, nobody has ever told them how to pay attention. They have to 'pay' attention and it is very expensive for them, because if they 'pay' attention their bodies become tense, and instead of becoming receptive to the teacher, they close themselves up. Somehow we have to teach them how to open up their ears, their minds, and for that they surely have to keep quiet. The big problem we teachers have to face is that children find it hard to stay motionless. If we want them to learn we have to somehow keep them quiet, but not tense.
- When the teacher is watching the class all the time he sees what is happening in the class – one child is not listening,

another is moving, etc., and then he gets very tense himself. He cannot relax at all because he has to watch out all the time.

- The teacher also has to speak a lot, and speaking is an act, it is not just doing nothing. When you speak for a long time your mouth becomes dry, you have to concentrate and speak up so everyone can hear you. Some teachers have never learned how to cultivate their voice. This is an art. If you become an actor, or speak on television, not only as a professional singer, you have to know how to direct and pitch your voice. Teachers lose too much energy through their speech and that is another reason why they get so tired and depressed. However, if you practise chanting Om aloud at least 24 times per day every day, then you develop your voice naturally. That is what I found. I never took lessons in diction but I found that my voice also changed for the better. So I lose less energy in my job because I use my vocal cords in a better way. Now I can speak for hours on end without getting tired.

Another reason why yoga helps is that the teacher learns to understand the nature of children better. We have been taught by the science of yoga that there is no separation of body and mind, but in our profession we tend to consider the schoolboy or schoolgirl as being minds. This can be symbolized by the fact that children are kept sitting and only the upper parts of their bodies are visible – we don't care about the rest. Besides they have to raise their hands. The child is cut into two parts: the upper one must react, the lower one is non-existent.

If we had to reduce the child to something it would be the brain, but we do nothing to cultivate the brain. The brain is not just an abstract tool of intellect, but a physical organ, so it is most important that it be irrigated with fresh oxygenated blood. It is a scientific fact that the brain needs more oxygen than any other organ in the body. So what do we do? Children are kept sitting nearly all the time, so how can the brain be well irrigated?

Harmonizing the whole personality

It is no surprise to see that children in France and many other countries are rebelling against the system. We have to do something about it urgently. Everybody in France feels involved in trying to change the system – that is the latest fashion. We talk a lot about changing the educational system and I think that yoga will play a role in these changes because we have a standpoint to evolve, a diagnosis about what is wrong. The point is that in yoga we consider the child to have more than one 'body', and these 'bodies' have to be harmonized. I will give a few examples:

- The child has eaten too much chocolate and the next day he has a mathematics class. He wants to listen because he likes the teacher, after all the teacher is very nice, and he must learn maths because his parents have told him that without maths he will not get a good job. So he wants to listen to the lesson but, "Oh, too much chocolate!". That is a point which cannot be evaded, if the physical body is not harmonized with the intellect there will be a problem.
- Another example is a child who has been running and playing in the physical education class. He arrives at the English or maths class and his breathing is uneven, he is breathless. A lot of material will pass him by unheard. He cannot concentrate because of the physiological upsurge. So the breathing has to be smoothed to enable him to listen and concentrate.
- Another example relates to the mental body. The evening before he has watched a football match, or a Dracula film, or 'The Bride of Frankenstein', or something like that. The following day he remembers it during the class. His mental energies are totally engaged elsewhere. While the teacher is explaining something or asking questions the child is not there, he is 'absent-minded'. Some people can still remember the visions and daydreams they used to have at their school benches.
- A last example concerns the problems which so many children have within their families. This will also disturb

their ability to memorize. So the physical, emotional and mental layers of the personality must be harmonized so that teaching can be efficient.

If the deep aspiration to grow and to learn, which has always existed in the mind, is covered by layers of tensions, and is not heeded and taken care of by the teacher, then the child will not be able to concentrate. Yoga exercises will help him to cope with these difficulties and that is why we often start the class in a revolutionary manner, that is with short breathing sessions.

It is not as simple as it looks, however, because breathing exercises might be needed more in the course of the class rather than at the beginning of the period. A teacher or educator must always have an eye on the reaction of his pupils. If he sees that the children are getting tired or bored, then he must immediately introduce something new. One must intersperse the class with different and varied exercises. Children love movement and variety and they cannot endlessly repeat the same exercises. A teacher would meet with failure if he did not use a lot of tricks to prevent dullness in his class. Children want change and entertainment and if they find it boring, don't worry, they will let you know. So part of my job was to devise and create a whole scale of different exercises for introduction into the normal classroom.

Education with a yogic vision

A teacher of yoga for children must sit in front of the children just as a musician sits in front of his piano. He has a lot of keys, black and white, and he must play his tune according to the situation, according to the time, according to the age group. He will have a lot of music pieces ready at his command. For instance, not everything can be done with older children. For kindergarten children you will not present the exercises in the same way as you do when you have fifteen-year-old teenagers.

At present many people are involved in research on the subject of yoga for children. I found my inspiration from

Swami Satyananda's impulse but anyone can find his own source of inspiration. What I want to stress is that a teacher must understand both the principles of yoga and the nature of the child. He must be very clear about what education amounts to. There is a very deep relationship between yoga and education. After all, yogis have always asserted that the human being is not yet human, but only a superior animal for the time being, but with and through yoga he can really become a human and evolve.

When we have children we want them to grow. If we are educators and yogis, we keep in mind the goal of all these parental and educational concerns. Where are we going? That idea is lacking nowadays in normal educational systems. There are techniques but there is no aim. We do not know what goals the human being tends towards. We think he just amounts to being a professional, that he is going to be an acrobat or a teacher or a doctor or a carpenter or a good for nothing, but we do not perceive a higher purpose apart from that. We have no refuge outside society. When the teacher or educator is a yogi, he can find a means because he has this higher purpose in mind. If you know quite well where you are going, then ways will come to you, but if you have no idea about what a truly humanizing upbringing amounts to, then you may have many techniques but they will not work. If the will is wrong, the ways cannot be right.

Finally, the state of evolution of the teacher is most important, and I trust you will check that first. Before any attempt is made to change the class, the teacher should try to change his own life through self-discipline. His renewed vision will be then translated into a fresh way of education.

9

Yoga and Education

Swami Yogabhakti Saraswati

In 1976 I held a meeting at my school to inform the parents, as well as the officials from the French Board of Education, about the experiments I was intending to start regarding yoga at school.

Here is a passage from the report of the first meeting: "The object of this meeting was to inform the parents of these pupils who practise exercises for well-being directly inspired by yoga that, within the framework of education, an experiment was to be held by Miss Flak (the author) and a team of teachers on the following theme: *Attempt to regain tranquility and to increase the faculties of concentration and attention of pupils by using short yoga exercises before the lessons.*"

Some doctors were also present at the time. Now, seven years later, it seems that yoga has gained more attention from the officials, for they now accept that such exercises can help the children develop their memory and attention, i.e., increase their learning faculties.

Yoga is of course a means to supreme well-being. However, if I were to have gone to the minister and said, "My aim in fostering yoga at school is to make the children attain samadhi", then I am sure that I would have frightened all the officials, and this would have been quite a normal reaction. Whilst teaching yoga at school we must not forget that the foremost aim of teaching is to enhance learning. Therefore, if we can develop the necessary qualities of learning then assuredly we will demonstrate that yoga is a useful subject.

Developing attention and awareness

We must be somewhat utilitarian in our approach while being faithful to our sources. Swami Satyananda and all the other great masters have always repeated: "Be aware", that is, "Be attentive". And this is precisely the quality which is required in order to learn well. So if we develop attention in children, then we develop a very useful quality for self-development, and at the same time we increase their powers of memory. As a result they learn more quickly and efficiently. This is what I tell the officials when I have to show them what yoga at school is all about. I assert that ultimately the aim of yoga is not different from the aim of education and that the children will derive from yoga a lot of techniques which have been tested by time.

There is no doubt that, with regard to the management of the intellect, we as educators and yogis have much to teach. For instance, it is a fact that some yogis have developed an extraordinary memory. There are many examples of people who have a photographic memory, not only as a gift from birth but because they have developed it by their own efforts. For example, near the end of the last century, while he was travelling in the USA to present yoga to the West, Swami Vivekananda went into a library. There he borrowed an encyclopaedia only the day before he was to leave the country. The librarian was somewhat surprised and asked if he were going to read it all; of course she was jesting. He replied that he had time to do so since he had twelve hours that night. The next day he returned the encyclopaedia and told the librarian that he had read it all. Whereupon she suggested that this was not possible. He then asked her to open the book at random and he repeated the whole page without making one mistake.

This is, of course, extraordinary but it shows that yogis probably have some secrets about developing the faculties of learning. Without attempting to go as far as Swami Vivekananda, we can be assured that by developing the quality of attention, of awareness, and using some of the exercises devised by the rishis and masters, we can help children learn better at school.

Recent scientific experiments have shown that memory can be enhanced by a certain attitude or a certain quality of consciousness. Some research has been done on the hormones which are present in the body at the time of learning. Different hormones correspond to different glands and these also correspond to different states of consciousness. There is a hormone of anger as well as a hormone of well-being. In the same way there are certain neurotransmitters which are released into the bloodstream when people are developing certain memories.

Drs Agranoff and Davis from the University of Michigan carried out an experiment on fish which will illustrate this point. The fish were swimming around in a tank and were to be taught not to bump into a glass partition which had been placed across the middle of the tank. There were two groups of fish. In the first group, the fish were taught not to bump into the glass and were allowed to swim around freely for a while after the learning period. The second group of fish were taught not to bump into the glass in the same way, but were also given an electric shock after the session.

All the fish from the two groups were studied. The results showed that the fish in the first group, which were allowed to relax and to continue swimming after the learning period, retained the neurotransmitter in the blood which is secreted during the learning experience. In the second group, which had been given an electric shock, the mind could not hold the memory and the blood did not retain the memory neurotransmitter. So the second group could not remember their lesson.

This and other studies indicate that relaxation is necessary to enhance memory. It is in a relaxed atmosphere that people remember best what they need to learn. This atmosphere of relaxation is something which has been particularly developed in ashrams. Relaxation is not only good for health, it is also good for learning.

Another point is that in yoga, relaxation is associated with a state of alertness. Usually in the West, people think of relaxation as a period of inactivity when the person concerned is somewhat absent-minded, no longer really aware. This is completely false. According to the principles of yoga it is possible to associate vigilance with relaxation, this is a perfect yogic state and it is also the best one for learning.

The Lozanov method of learning

Nowadays, techniques such as the Lozanov method, known as suggestopaedia, are founded upon exactly the same principles. Dr Lozanov, a Bulgarian, set up a school in Sofia where experiments have been made in learning languages in a three month period instead of the usual three years. The principles used in that method are similar to those used by yogis for developing greater awareness. This suggestopaedia method is very close to yoga and to my mind it is one of the best methods ever devised to improve learning. For this method to be successful the following points are important:

Creating an atmosphere: Creating an atmosphere of calm enjoyment and at the same time stimulating the right amount of excitement and alertness is essential. It is very important that the classroom should reflect the attitudes which the teacher himself has as a result of practising yoga. The teacher, like the captain of a ship, is responsible for creating the appropriate atmosphere.

Developing all the senses: Another aspect that yoga teaches is that all the senses should be used in learning. Our system develops the eyes and the ears. Children must look at things, read, find out what is interesting in the pictures or texts, and they must listen. The ears and eyes are no doubt very important but what about touch, smell and taste? These seem to have disappeared from the classroom. Since we learn through the eyes and ears, why can't we learn from touch, movement, smell and taste? This is important, especially with very small children.

Creating the right balance between introversion and extroversion: An important fact which educators must keep in mind when teaching yoga to children is this: whereas an adult practising yoga must learn how to introvert, the newborn child who has been protected by his mother's womb and is in direct contact with the self through his unconscious mind, must now learn to feel the presence of the outside world and to become extroverted. After this process is over he will learn to introvert again.

It would be a mistake to introvert a small child, what he needs is to develop his senses and know the outside world. A yogi must understand that process and not make children who want to move about, sit quiet all the time, close their eyes etc., since this would create an imbalance in the child's personality. This is the reason why those who teach yoga to children should understand that the awareness of the child is very different from the awareness of an adult. They should not try to introvert the children too much, except where concentration is needed or after periods of excitement.

The new system of education through yoga and other means can only evolve if people are aware of the nature of the child. It cannot be devised from a consideration of the nature of an adult. Formerly, people treated children just as if they were little adults. If we look at seventeenth and eighteenth century paintings we can see children dressed as little men and women. Nowadays it has been reversed, and adults seem to consider themselves as children! They even have toys which they call gadgets! Of course it is no less difficult for them than previous generations to understand the nature of the child. It is, therefore, necessary for the yogi to study the processes involved when the human being is in a state of continuous growth. It should also be realized that this growth should be nurtured and checked where necessary so that balance may be created between introversion and extroversion.

Recognizing types of attention: In order to increase alertness it is necessary for the teacher to recognize the four types of attention.

1. *Slack attention, known as tamasic*: The whole face usually has a dull and slack expression, signifying lack of interest and apathy. The eyes can be partly closed or turned up to one side with a faraway look. At times the child may frown or look quite docile. The hair and overall appearance can sometimes look messy through the child's general indifference. This is an indication of a child who needs much more stimulating rather than tranquilizing exercises. This child is a good child, but is daydreaming.
2. *Uneven attention, known as rajasic*: The eyes are darting here and there. The tongue and teeth are frequently moving, either biting or licking the lips. The mouth or whole face can change expression from one minute to the next. The hair can also be untidy through nervously playing with it. This child reacts to the slightest noise but the dissipated mind quickly jumps to the next disturbance. This is characteristic of 'fidgety' children, the most common type these days. We might judge this type of child to be hyperactive due to the predominance of the sympathetic system. He is interested, but superficially; his attention span is short and he wastes his energy by spending it indiscriminately. These children need relaxing exercises and learning how to relax will be extremely beneficial for them.
3. *Concentrated attention, known as sattwic*: Here the eyes are more concentrated; they look obviously absorbed in the lesson or activity and are not daydreaming. Sometimes the mouth looks a little tight, with the cheeks drawn in slightly, as if concentrating with some tension. This expression is usually held for a long period of time, without the constant facial movements of the rajasic child.
   This is found in the 'good' children who are lucky enough to possess a well-balanced neurovegetative system which makes learning easy for them. They are able to work hard

regularly; they listen well and their answers are relevant. Their attentiveness and calm may also be associated with enthusiasm and creativity. These are two essential qualities in the assessment of a child's stability. If the child is too conforming and tied to routine, this may be a negative aspect.

4. *Perfect attention*: Eyes are completely bright, sparkling and alert. There is often a smile and the facial muscles are relaxed – no tension. The child's reactions are usually spontaneous, appropriate and confident.

   This is the highest form of the classifications we have made, but also the most uncommon. It may be found in children gifted with exceptional intelligence and powers of concentration. Children have to be attentive and in the description above you can see the different types of attention which a teacher must recognize. The teacher himself must be attentive in order to know what type of exercises he should introduce into his class at any time.

If the student is tamasic, that is, indolent, then the teacher will have to introduce techniques of a dynamic nature. If, on the other hand, the child acts like a monkey, he is rajasic, and the teacher will have to introduce relaxation exercises. If the child is rather concentrated then he will need to give balancing exercises that are equally good for relaxation and vigilance. If he finds he has a child who is a genius, he will not need any exercises; the child will progress by himself.

There are also moments during the class which can be described as tamasic, rajasic, sattwic and genius moments. Thus, Monday morning at 8.30 a.m. is a tamasic moment, while on Friday afternoon at 4 p.m. the children will correspond to the rajasic type. The teacher must select from the large variety of exercises those which are suitable for the moment and this is something a yoga teacher must be keen to learn.

Straightening the children's backs: It has been found that the level of a person's energy is in direct relationship with the structure of the spine. This is not just a matter of well-adjusted vertebrae but of a pole along which the life impulses, comparable to electricity, are ascending to the brain and feeding our attention and zest for living. Nowadays, children are not taught properly how to sit and stand erect and, therefore, correcting their backs should be an important item of yoga at school. Instead of harping on again and again about sitting erect, why not introduce a number of joyful occasions to make them aware of their spines?

10

Questions and Answers

Swami Satyananda Saraswati

At what age should children start yoga classes?

At the age of eight teach them surya namaskara, mantra and pranayama. These three practices should be continued for several years until the signs of puberty appear. Then change the practices and give them more asanas and pranayama. If the child starts these three practices at the age of eight, puberty will naturally be delayed for two or three years. Usually puberty takes place between twelve and fourteen, and is established between fourteen and sixteen, but if the child practises yoga, puberty will start at fourteen and be established at eighteen. When the signs of puberty appear, the child can take up all major asanas.

Meditation techniques should be taught after the age of twenty-one. This applies to those children who have been practising yoga from the age of eight. Up to the age of twenty-one they should use simple methods of meditation, such as kirtan, chanting and visualization.

I thought that these practices were only given to boys. Can girls also do them?

It is not correct to say that these practices were not meant for girls. In the vedic age, both boys and girls were initiated into sandhya and Gayatri. It was only later, during the period of our cultural decadence, that this amendment was made. Girls can definitely practise Gayatri mantra.

Are mantras and music helpful for children?

Relaxing the brain through mantra is one of the methods of increasing perception, but yantra is a more direct method because it is a process of awakening, not a process of relaxing. Some systems use music to help children relax. This is not bad, but it creates a certain amount of inactivity. Most music makes the mind inactive, although some types of music make it expressive and other types are very awakening for children. Visualization of yantra is, however, a totally dynamic, activating method. When you practise awareness of the yantra, your mind is continually generating higher wave patterns, it is never regressing. Concentration on a particular yantra stimulates a similar archetype in the brain, which creates an awakening at a higher level.

So our efforts should keep the process of awakening active in the brain. I know about music and I like it, but it tends to make the mind inactive. Inactivity cannot be the objective of yoga, especially when the purpose is to awaken the potentialities in the child. Every practice we teach children should create a movement or an event of awakening in them. This does not mean that music is not included in the scheme of yoga. If music is practised correctly, it stimulates its own archetypes in the brain. It can create a gradual awakening in the structure of the brain, but first we have to define what we mean by music. If the music is unsystematic or sexually stimulating, we do not know what it will do.

Is it good for a child of two to learn mantra?

No. It is better not to teach the child yet, but instead you can practise yourself those things you would like him to learn. If you are chanting the Upanishads, practising mantra or meditation, and getting up at 4 or 5 a.m. each day, the child will imbibe all these positive habits because he is like a photo camera. Children are definitely influenced by the structure of their environment and the personalities surrounding them. If you cry, shout and scream, what can you teach your children? If you are nervous, depressed and easily excited, what example do you set for your children? Those things you wish to teach your children are what you are badly lacking yourself. Therefore, the best thing to do is to live the way you would like your children to live and they will imbibe your lifestyle.

Should yoga be taught to children, or should it be left to their own choice?

If you are going to leave yoga to the children's choice then you should leave everything to their choice. Children are pliable, innocent and devoted. They believe in higher realities but they need proper training. It is better to give them an education in spiritual life, discipline and yoga from the very beginning. When both parents and children follow a disciplined and regular lifestyle, it will ultimately reflect in the behaviour and personality of a nation. Your nation, government and family are your pride and that pride is discipline. All the achievements of America, Germany, Russia and China have been brought about through discipline. The first yoga sutra of Patanjali is "*Atha yoga anushasanam*", which means yoga is discipline. It doesn't even say yoga is practice. Give your children discipline but only little by little. If you press a pencil too hard the lead will break. Give your children discipline in the light of a spiritual and yogic education.

What can we do to counteract bad influences?

Family life has a great influence on the child, so the first thing that must be done is to reintegrate family culture. The family structure has been undergoing a process of disintegration for the last twenty years, but now we must stop it and start emphasizing the correct way of family life. The greatest corrective influence on children is other children. If a child is wrong and other children tell him so, the child will think about it, but he will not care if the parents tell him.

Secondly, the schools need some sort of reorientation. In India we have the example of the gurukul system, where children live in ashrams with the guru for several years.

They are far from the city and manage the whole school themselves. They wake up early, have their morning bath, pray and perform their exercises and duties.

Are there any general rules in yoga for bringing up children?

Parents worry too much about their children. Children must be left with other children; they must be left to grow on their own. The duty of the parents is to take care of them as long as they are innocent, so that they don't get into trouble. I have seen, and most of you will agree, that parents worry so much about their children that the children go wrong.

How should parents encourage good habits and discourage bad ones?

You must set an example, and the children will follow it. When the child is in the womb, you can train him there rather than trying to change and brainwash him when he is born. Life in the womb is more powerful and more receptive because you can change the entire structure of the deoxyribonucleic acid (DNA) molecules.

How should we bring children up so they do not become egotistic and aggressive?

Children should not be suppressed. The personality must grow, the ego must develop, but you can create a way for their spiritual advancement. You can do that either by living a spiritual life yourself or else by letting them follow their own nature without any obstruction from your side. We should not try to force or build children into our own patterns, or modify their personalities. They must follow their nature.

When should yoga be integrated into the school?

Yoga can be taught in easily understandable terms from class five to university level, step by step, by teachers who have made a thorough study of the subject and have undergone special training.

Along what lines should the educational system be reorientated?

The school system should be based on self-discipline rather than the enforcement of outer discipline. This requires that the teacher imbibes the yogic philosophy in order to increase his own inner power and thereby inspire discipline in others. This is more effective and lasting.

Do you agree that the poor quality of students is due to the poor quality of the teachers?

I do agree, but the poor quality of students may also be attributed to the poor quality of the parents. It may be due to degeneration in genetics, poor environment, the way the children are brought up, the lack of respect and understanding they receive, etc. All these factors count.

Can yoga help juvenile delinquents?

This is a very important topic. Why do children start behaving antisocially and committing all sorts of criminal acts? There are many reasons given by different people, but I have my own theory. At the age of seven or eight years, the pineal gland in the child begins to decay, to calcify, and with that a major controlling lock upon the function of the pituitary gland is released. When this control is released the pituitary hormones begin to form and enter the bloodstream. Aggressive, antisocial and delinquent behaviour, which signals the onset of puberty and sexual activity, can arise at any time after the pineal gland has begun this process of decay. However, as long as the pineal gland is kept in a healthy condition and not allowed to decay, this dawning of sexual consciousness, which follows the release of pituitary hormones will be delayed.

Nowadays, as children grow up, their pineal gland begins to decay and their pituitary gland begins to develop automatically. As a result they have high levels of different disturbing hormones in their blood which influence the different glands and the nervous system, ultimately affecting their behaviour. This causes an imbalance between their mental and vital fields. 'Vital' means prana, the bioenergy; and 'mental' means mind. The pranic and mental fields are unable to coordinate with each other and the glands such as the thyroid and adrenals do not work in absolute coordination with each other.

The sexual secretions usually start after a certain point of physical maturity. Nowadays they start earlier, before the child possesses the mental and emotional stability to cope with such powerful hormonal drives. In these cases the children start developing different types of ideas which do not find any control or counterbalance to act in opposition.

Every individual has a controlling factor within. If you want to murder someone, you think about it, but after some time another thought comes which opposes the previous one. There is always a conflict there, and this is called a control. It is a measure of maturity. If you want to drink poison in order to commit suicide, at the same time you think, "no", then "yes", and "no" again, and it continues in this way. This does not happen with some of these children who get a single idea and hang onto it indiscriminately. They ignore the shakti of viveka (discrimination). There is no power of discrimination because physical, hormonal and mental maturity are yet to be developed.

The adrenal glands are very important and have a wide range of influence on the human body. The thyroid gland is also a very significant gland which plays an important role in the emotions of human life, like fear and love. If there is an imbalance in these glands, what is going to happen to the children? Their behaviour is affected by the disordered development of these glands.

So, in yoga, the first thing to be done is to keep the pineal gland healthy for as long as possible. As long as your pineal gland is healthy your sexual glands will remain under control. As long as the sex glands remain under control there will not be a toxic effect in the body, because the sex glands produce those particular secretions which are toxic in nature. They can create physical diseases and even insanity. That is why there is a system of marriage, because through that system you are able to get these toxic secretions out of the physical body harmlessly, and we are all the products of these toxins. If you were to develop these secretions at a very tender age, when you had not yet developed intellectual, emotional, and physical maturity, what would happen to your mental balance? Just imagine if a boy of twelve was able to know as much as I know? What would be the state of his mental balance? There would be no coordination or balance between the physical, mental and emotional factors during the tender years when the pineal gland is destroyed. Children would become juvenile delinquents.

This problem was avoided in ancient India, where children were initiated into three particular yogic practices at the age of seven or eight. One practice was surya namaskara and the other two were pranayama and Gayatri mantra. Today this tradition continues with the sacred thread ceremony but unfortunately few people understand the meaning and importance of the initiation. They consider it just a social ritual and do not take it seriously. However, these are yogic practices which should be taught to children at the age when the pineal gland starts to deteriorate so they can keep balance with the disturbing factors within their developing bodies.

My child suffers from cystic fibrosis, a pancreatic disease. Can you suggest a practice?

In this case I think you should start with the practice of yoga nidra. When the child goes off to bed, within a minute you should start teaching him mantra. He will recite the mantra and gradually he will enter into a deep sleep. Disturb his sleep a little bit and then tell him to go on repeating the mantra. He will just repeat half and will then again go off into slumber. Disturb him again and continue disturbing him for a further ten minutes. He will turn onto his side and do all sorts of things. In the morning when he wakes up, ask him, "Do you know which mantra I taught you last night? It is good for you and will help you improve." Repeat the same thing for fifteen days.

You should first of all treat sickness which has gone into the deeper mind. One is physically sick and one knows that one is physically sick, and that knowledge again feeds the sickness. "I am sick, I am sick", is repeated more or less consciously. So first cut off, disconnect the knowledge and the awareness. In many cases, only half the sickness will remain, or sometimes even less and sometimes it will be removed altogether.

Sickness is not always physical, it can be anything. The parents' mental condition may have begun the child's sickness. It is very mysterious; we cannot prove it but that can be the cause. Parents' nervousness and their misbehaviour with each other, or their mental formations, or just the physical factors in the child may be the cause. It is very difficult to say. So it is much better to treat it first at a deeper level by using mantra repetition in this way.

Choose any mantra which the child can repeat. However, he should not understand what this mantra actually is, because if he does understand it then the intellectual process begins. The intellectual process must be avoided as far as possible. So do this for fifteen days. After that you can start giving him the easy asanas such as surya namaskara, siddhasana, padmasana. Children will respond very positively to yoga practices.

At what age should you teach pranayama to children?

After seven years, but with no retention. Do not teach kumbhaka, retention of breath. Breathing in and breathing out only is enough.

Can one teach bhramari pranayama between the ages of two and a half and four years?

Yes, it helps them and children like to make the humming sound '*mm-mm-mm-mm...*'

I teach a class of children and adults in which three of the adults are mentally disturbed. Am I harming the children?
No, give them inner visualization practices, dharana. Let them lie down or sit and start visualization. Pretend there is a blackboard with white or red or blue or yellow chalk. On the blackboard they write 1, 2, 3, with white chalk. Now write 4, 5, 6, with the red chalk, then change to blue and write 7, 8, 9, 10. Try to make them visualize it as you are telling them. Change fairly fast, not slowly, 1, 2, 3, change chalk, 4, 5, 6, change chalk, 7, 8, 9, 10. They have to be efficient; do not give time for mental dissipation or drowsiness.

There are many objects for visualization, but easier ones must come first, like numbers, then perhaps geometrical symbols. Geometrical designs are used in tantra and have a very great effect on the human mind. You can permute and combine these geometrical designs or yantras, and it will help these people very much. For example, first visualize an upright triangle, then an inverted triangle: one is blue, one is yellow, one is red, one is white. Within the triangle there is another triangle and another two triangles intersecting each other, then a circle inside with another point at the centre, then another circle outside. This can be developed depending on the efficiency of the mind.

Let them also visualize scenery, such as beautiful lakes and oceans, waves and clouds, some black and white clouds looking like rabbits, a horse, a demon or dragon, the stars, but not the sun and moon which children cannot handle. Later when you know that they have become very sensitive ask them to visualize waves of air. You cannot see air, but you can feel it and experience its fragrances.

First take them deeper and deeper with gross symbols. Start with easier ones on a blackboard. You can also tell them to feel as if they have some plain paper or a stitched notebook, with a ballpoint pen, a fountain pen or a felt pen; it doesn't matter. They should write in numerals, the alphabet, or their own names, once in blue, then in red, then in yellow. Their power of visualization will improve. Maybe that is how a photographic memory develops.

a random line of children and adults in which three of the adults are mentally disturbed. [illegible]

[illegible]

[illegible] for the thickness of the mould.

[illegible]

[illegible] then to red, then to yellow. Then [illegible]

Yoga as Therapy

11

Yoga for Emotional Disturbances

Swami Bodhananda Saraswati

The first years of life provide the foundation of adulthood. Emotionally disturbed children become severely neurotic adults, who in turn raise neurotic offspring. Whether you are a parent, a teacher, a doctor, or a childcare worker, if you are dealing with emotionally disturbed children, you have already realized the scope and diversity of this problem. Children may suffer emotional handicaps for biological, cultural or social reasons and frequently with a combination of symptoms. Accurate diagnosis cannot be overemphasized; it is the only way to avoid incorrect treatment. Yoga offers a practical form of therapy to deal with the problems of abnormal emotional development, so that the child may reach adulthood free from personality disorders. The function of the pineal gland, the importance of balancing mental and pranic energies, the use of yoga nidra and karma yoga, as well as reduction of family and social pressures – all these factors must be considered in dealing with the disturbed child. These simple therapeutic practices, used in conjunction with psychological understanding, point the way to a new and integrated approach for treating emotional disturbance.

Psychiatrically disturbed children

In her book, *Children Under Stress*, Dr Sula Wolff speaks about preventative psychiatry as a way of ameliorating the needless neurotic illnesses of later life. This involves a careful scrutiny of the child's environment, so that those stresses and deprivations known to cause psychiatric disorders can be lessened or removed.

Everywhere educators are realizing the social responsibility they hold in providing an atmosphere conducive to the development of independent, self-disciplined and well-balanced children. Learning is exponentially cumulative. Therefore, we should exercise discrimination to ensure that schools are not simply information factories geared to the production of robot-like individuals for the maintenance of the consumer society. Children involved in a creative learning process, centred on the methods of active inquiry and discovery, are less likely to feel bored, frustrated and depressed. If they are immersed in stimulating, challenging projects, how can they feel anxious or threatened?

Children, however, do develop neurotic and psychiatric illnesses, therefore we cannot ignore the school environment, where the pressure to achieve and conform may prove to be an overwhelming stress to some children. An exceptionally intelligent child who is forced to endure years of boring lessons, with no avenue for creative expression, may resort to obsessive behaviour or a fantasy world. A naturally aggressive child, when deprived of physical learning activities, will become extremely disruptive and destructive.

Psychiatric disturbances in children may be linked to premature sexual maturation where the nervous system and hormonal secretions are imbalanced, or they may be related to parental rejection, family repression, or chronic physical ailments. The disturbed child needs to alleviate his anxiety and guilt, and drop his defence mechanisms, so that normal personality growth can continue. Here, a skilled yoga therapist can prescribe relaxation practices such as yoga nidra, to release repressed feelings from the unconscious mind. During therapy a child requires a trusting adult with whom he feels secure enough to ventilate his feelings. If he only meets with punishment and disapproval then emotions remain repressed and symptoms continue to build up.

The delinquent child

Children who are labelled socially maladjusted or delinquent have often suffered early deprivation or maternal rejection, as many studies have shown. Their antisocial behaviour reflects a lack of conscience and a need for love. What they really need is a good parent, but often their unacceptable behaviour leads them into institutions where the only concept of therapy is authoritarian discipline, meted out through strict supervision and punishment. The children obey out of fear, but when they leave the institution their personal view of the world and themselves has not changed, and they take their revenge on society in the perpetration of various crimes.

Autocratic discipline, externally applied, is virtually useless with this type of child. A comparative study of delinquent boys living in Wiltwyck Community School in New York, with boys living in a rigidly disciplined reformatory, demonstrated the superiority of a therapeutic community setting, where virtues of trust and understanding were upheld. At the end of their stay, boys in the reform school were more anxious, prejudiced and resentful of authority, while Wiltwyck boys were less anxious, and happier with themselves and their teachers. It seems that punishing a child is not a positive means of bringing about change or reform.

How can we utilize the practices of yoga to reform delinquent children? We cannot replace the parent, but through yoga techniques we can teach the child how to resolve his personal conflicts. Teachers of delinquent children should undertake the practice of yoga themselves, and then begin to introduce it to the children in their charge. The teachers may also find certain yoga techniques useful in maintaining the high energy level required in working with delinquent children.

Many delinquent children have pent-up feelings of anger and aggression. For them, karma yoga should be provided to help release and rechannel their energies in a more constructive way. Woodworking, painting or gardening are a few avenues available. For a child who suffers extreme anger, the practice of shashankasana is most helpful. This stops the flow of excess hormones from the adrenal glands, which are responsible for the loss of self-control. Practices such as nadi shodhana pranayama and yoga nidra will provide much needed relaxation and restore the balance of mental and pranic energy.

Delinquent children really benefit most from an extended period of ashram life. In this highly charged atmosphere, such children are truly reformed and often blossom into most competent and useful members of society. In lieu of ashram training, a competent yoga teacher can be instrumental in instilling a higher self-concept and an attitude of inner discipline.

The role of the pineal gland

The pineal is a tiny gland, located in the medulla oblongata of the brain. In yoga it is closely linked with ajna chakra, the seat of wisdom and intuition. When the child is about eight years of age, the pineal begins to degenerate. This decay corresponds to the beginning of sexual maturation, precipitated by the release of hormones from the pituitary gland. Many children do not cope well during this transitional period, when sexual awareness is developing. Therefore, disruptive behaviour is often evinced at this age, such as anger, resentment, or violence, much of which can be directly or indirectly attributed to hormonal imbalance.

Why burden a child with sexual responsibility at such a tender age? If we can find a way to delay the decay of the pineal gland and to maintain a balance between the sympathetic (pingala) and the parasympathetic (ida) nervous systems, then the child can continue to experience childhood without the stress of inappropriate impulses.

In yogic terminology, emotional disturbance is the result of an imbalance of manas shakti (the mental component) and prana shakti (the vital component). Where there is excess mental energy and a lack of prana, the child suffers withdrawal, depression, anxiety or lethargy. He lacks dynamism and cannot transform his mental energy into creative action. Conversely, if the child has excess prana and not enough manas, then he will become very destructive and disruptive. A vast amount of energy with no control spells disaster. It is comparable to a fast moving vehicle with no brakes. Such hyperactive children are difficult to live with, and learning is almost impossible for them in this state.

Yoga as preventive medicine

A few simple practices starting from the age of eight will help to balance the mental and vital energies and preserve the pineal gland, thus delaying sexual maturation and preventing needless psychoemotional distress. The child can be taught surya namaskara, a dynamic exercise involving twelve different movements. This provides stretching and relaxation for the body, and helps to rebalance the energy. He can practise shambhavi mudra, focusing the gaze on the eyebrow centre, which is essential for maintaining the health of the pineal gland. Nadi shodhana pranayama balances the nadis and nervous system, and teaches the child how to induce calmness within himself.

In dealing with emotionally unstable children, we must remember that they are not necessarily receptive, cooperative or obedient, and a person attempting to teach them yoga practices may easily become frustrated when confronted by a negative, resentful child. The key point is to remain objective. The child may be defiant and show anger and hostility, but he is likely to be using the instructor to express the anger he feels for someone else, perhaps his mother or father. In any case, yoga cannot be forced on anyone, so it is up to the adult to devise ways of introducing these techniques so that they appeal to the imagination of the child. If the child can experience even a brief period of mental relaxation, he will gain some insight into his own behaviour.

For emotionally distressed children, who find inactivity almost unbearable, the combination of physical movement and progressive relaxation is most appropriate. After surya namaskara the child will willingly lie down in shavasana for yoga nidra. Following the progressive relaxation of body parts, the instructor may run through a series of visualizations such as 'an elephant', 'house', 'black dog', and so on. The purpose of the exercise is to induce deep relaxation, so that negative impressions locked in the unconscious mind will float to the surface and be dissipated. The total practice period should take no more than ten minutes a day. Children under the age of eight do not need surya namaskara or pranayama practices, but simple yoga nidra techniques can be introduced with good effect.

12

Yoga for the Disabled

Swami Nishchalananda Saraswati

Yoga has its role to play in the lives of people of all denominations, ages and nationalities, whether disabled or not. For those who are disabled, however, it has particular benefit because it works on three levels – the physical, the mental and the spiritual, and maintains an integrated development.

Alleviation of the physical problem

The exact application of yoga techniques depends largely on individual physical disability. If a limb is missing or very deformed, then of course the best initial treatment is likely to be the application of medical engineering to provide an artificial limb or assist the functioning of one that is defective. However, yoga asanas and pranayama can often be utilized to improve sluggish blood circulation in defective limbs, to improve and stimulate nerve functions and to develop weak muscles and bring them under conscious control.

Many disabled children come to our ashrams, and usually by tailoring yogic practices to their individual needs, much is gained in the overall health of the body. Though our example will be of young adults, the same principles will apply to children. For example, a young man of seventeen who came to our ashram had practically lost the use of both legs. He had previously been able to hobble around on his knees, but even this capacity had been lost. His distress was increased by the fact that through lack of exercise of the lower areas of the body, his blood circulation was very poor. This led to numbness and extreme discomfort. His lack of exercise had also led to stiffness and pain in the lower back. Over the next three weeks, he practised a series of special asanas adapted for his specific condition and within this short period all pain and numbness went, blood circulation was normalized and the limbs were regaining their normal function.

In another case, yoga therapy dramatically improved the condition of a young man who had been suffering from paralysis of both legs. This problem had arisen soon after he had been bitten by a dog and had been given the standard preventive treatment against rabies. Whether this was the cause or not is uncertain, but within one day he totally lost the use of his legs. He could not move them even slightly. He tried many remedies with no success and ultimately lost all hope. He came to the yoga ashram more as a desperate last resort than with any real belief that yoga would help him. Slowly, however, over a period of months, he regained the use of his limbs and now they are 90 percent normal. Today this man is jubilant and he has become an ardent supporter of the yogic science.

Polio is another common problem which has proved amenable to yogic treatment. With polio, the degree of improvement depends largely on the sincere efforts of the patient and the severity of the case. Yoga training from an expert is essential, and regularity in practise on the part of the patient is a must. For example, Madam Eva Riche-Paul who was afflicted by polio as a child, used yoga as a form of physiotherapy. Today, she is well known throughout Europe and has written many authoritative books on yoga. She maintained that it was not just constant practise of repetitive movements that helped in her physical rehabilitation, but it was the awareness of movement that was important. She said that ten rotations of a joint by a therapist had much less effect on rehabilitation than one rotation where there was total awareness of movement.

Mental health

The science of yoga is not only for the body, it is also for the mind. Even though a child or adult may be crippled in body, he or she is more than likely to be perfectly sound in mind. Yoga helps individuals develop their latent mental faculties and intelligence to the fullest possible extent.

Many disabled children have brilliant minds and the capacity to reach the highest degree levels. Yoga can definitely help them to realize their potential and to lead creative, productive lives, so that they can be of maximum use to themselves, their families and society as a whole. One disabled young man who often comes to our ashram has now earned an MA degree in English and has undertaken to teach others in his home. He has had great success in this endeavour and has gained much from yoga, both physically and mentally. He was in a state of depression and hopelessness before starting yoga practice; now he is bubbling with optimism and confidence about his life and his future.

Spiritual health

In spirit, there is no disability whatsoever. Many people who are physically disabled practise yoga in order to go deeper into themselves. Through yoga they find the way to free themselves, and they come to realize that there is much more to their nature than the limitations imposed upon them by a mere physical defect. Medical science has done wonders in this technological era and has achieved a high level of sophistication and utility. It should be combined with the science of yoga to further optimize the benefits that can be obtained by the disabled.

Kirtan

Kirtan is a method of using sound for focusing attention and developing aural perceptions. These sounds are normally produced by the person, either with his voice in singing or chanting, or with his hands or feet in keeping rhythm. Rhythm instruments may also be used for kirtan.

Kirtan is highly recommended in therapy for the disabled. At Camphill, Rudolf Steiner School, Aberdeen, a community for retarded and maladjusted children, the importance of music in the curriculum and the degree of appreciation the disabled children have for music is very obvious.

Music classes are held in two ways:

1. Once a week with a skilled musician who plays all kinds of tunes, using different instruments or inviting professionals to show their skills adjusted to the listener's needs.
2. Every day in their special school classes, their English teacher sings a morning prayer and some songs with them. They also sing a prayer before and after eating. The idea is that the children repeat, together with the adults, sounds of music with or without words.

There is a joyful Scottish song called 'The drunken sailor' and its tune very much resembles yogic kirtans. This song was a favourite of one teacher, who sang it everywhere in the school. Two children were beneficially influenced by this continuous singing until finally each sang at least one full verse of the song. One child was mentally retarded, very shy and unable to concentrate, and the other child was autistic, uttering only the word 'no'. It was a great experience to hear these children singing.

Since the importance of kirtan lies in the feelings of the heart and in personal expression regardless of the perfection usually required in singing, the introduction of kirtan in special cases, such as with disabled children, will prove an indispensable asset in their therapy.

13

Yoga Benefits Juvenile Diabetes

Dr Swami Karmananda Saraswati

A few years ago diabetes among children was a rare phenomenon. Diabetes was usually a disease of old age, first appearing in those around fifty or sixty years, who consumed too much sugar and starch in their diet, carried too much weight and did not exercise. This state of exhaustion of the pancreas can be controlled and restored by yoga therapy and dietary regulations which resensitize the body's tissues to its own insulin, rejuvenate the pancreas and digestive gland and restore correct body weight. We always have a few of these patients in the ashram, where they learn to stabilize their blood sugar levels through yogic practices.

However, times have changed and the spectrum of diabetes is changing. Medical students report that diabetes amongst children is increasing and we have also observed this in our research. Diabetes in children is increasing relentlessly today due to the imbalances which are evolving within the modern civilized lifestyle. The pattern of diabetes which emerges gradually in later life can be controlled by dietary and yogic practices, but this new trend in diabetes is more severe than diabetes which develops in old age.

According to medical science, juvenile diabetes requires insulin injections, and the children are trained to administer these injections themselves two or three times a day. Sometimes they are injecting up to 50 or 75 units. Unfortunately there are some side effects; the insulin is extracted from the pancreas of animals and those animal proteins act as a foreign stimulus or antigen to which the body's defence mechanisms react. Other drugs are also used to control blood sugar levels, but some will injure the heart. However, we have found that juvenile diabetics often respond to an extensive program of asanas, pranayama, shatkriyas and relaxation, if they spend a month or so in the ashram.

Causes of juvenile diabetes

To understand childhood diabetes, we have to first see how a child becomes diabetic. A child can be born with a pre-weakened or undeveloped pancreas or liver. This does not mean that it is an inherited disease, but that the foetus was either deprived of an important building material needed to construct the digestive glands, or was exposed to a dangerous poison, chemical or drug which crossed the placental barrier from the mother's bloodstream. This is one of the complications of our present technological lifestyle.

Nowadays, modern foods are artificially treated and preserved and many more drugs and tablets are consumed than in former times. Even the air we breathe and the water we drink are no longer natural and pure. Once we used to worry about infectious diseases spreading via our water supply, but now toxic chemicals pose a far greater risk to our health and welfare; our children are most sensitive to them.

Although the placenta does not allow poisons and infectious diseases to cross from the mother during foetal development, the placental barrier can be penetrated by many of the synthetic drugs and industrial chemicals which we are exposed to, and the developing liver and pancreas are extremely sensitive to these influences. This is why some babies are born with jaundice. Either the liver, pancreas and digestive apparatus are immature, or else the liver has been poisoned by a drug or toxin the mother has taken.

Another major cause of juvenile diabetes is an unsuitable diet during infancy and early childhood. This leads to premature exhaustion of the pancreas. Many parents have a false concept here. They want their children to grow as fast as animals whose lifespans are far shorter than our own. The age of full mature growth attainment has a definite relationship to overall lifespan. A human being is designed to complete his growth in twenty to twenty-five years while a cow is mature in two or three years.

When we give children a lot of animal proteins (such as milk, fish, meat and eggs), starches and sugars, the vital organs of digestion, assimilation and metabolism are overworked and prematurely exhausted. The best diet for the baby is mother's milk. It is a complete food in every way. Mothers should not be too anxious to wean their children. In some societies breastfeeding continues for up to two or three years. Therefore, the infant should be weaned from the breast gradually and introduced to fruit, vegetables and cooked grains. In infancy and childhood, it is especially important to nurture the developing pancreatic capacity by not overfeeding them with a huge intake of starch and sugar, in the form of sweetened, processed baby foods.

Emotional disturbances

Each case of juvenile diabetes is individual, so it is unwise to make generalized statements. Nevertheless, we have found that many juvenile diabetics have a history of an insecure early childhood. For one reason or another, the predominant emotional climate which has surrounded them from infancy has failed to adequately nurture, support and encourage them. It is a most potent cause of progressive malfunctioning of the secretory, endocrine and digestive glands.

After all, fear, threat and anger surely influences the digestive process. If you are about to eat and become incited to anger, the appetite vanishes immediately. The salivary glands fail to secrete and the mouth becomes dry. In the same way, the glands of the stomach, liver and pancreas also become inactive and the capacity to digest is lost. If the child's emotional environment is one of constant fear and threat, the digestive capacity can be permanently impaired.

Practices

14

Yoga Techniques for Pre-School Children

Arundhati

The setting and the sessions are two important aspects to consider when presenting yoga, especially if it is being incorporated into regular playgroup activities. Let us first consider the setting for these activities.

Place of practice: A space that is free from furniture or objects with sharp edges is necessary. It should be carpeted if possible but this is not absolutely necessary; small carpet pieces or a small towel, large enough for the child to sit on, will be enough.

Time of practice: The practice should not immediately follow a meal. Usually two hours are allowed between eating and starting yoga activities.

Length of practice: Children at this pre-school age normally have a fairly short concentration span; therefore, we need to time the exercises according to the children involved, always watching the children's involvement. The constant movement of arms and legs and not being able to sit still for any length of time – sudden spurts of 'mad' activity, rushing about aimlessly and useless repetitive movement patterns – all result from development taking place within the nervous system of the child and are major differences between the behaviour of adults and children. Usually, yoga sessions with children are about one hour in length. This does not mean that one is doing one activity for the whole hour. If the teacher is able to create an interesting atmosphere and keeps differing postures to a reasonable time span, the posture session alone can take 30 to 40 minutes with the children enjoying every minute.

Teaching aids

- *Pictures*: When lessons are presented and accompanied by visual aids, the learning process is enhanced and this is also true when learning through play. Not only are pictures a good source for labelling and classifying words, but they can lead to what one psychologist calls 'representation competence' the ability to recognize three-dimensional objects presented in flat two-dimensional form, which is an important skill for schoolwork. Since many asanas, or physical postures, done with children of this age have animal names, it is good to have pictures of these animals for them to see. Children in my classes have a notebook of their own in which they stick pictures of the different animals, flowers, objects and so forth.
- *Blackboard*: A blackboard is a very important teaching aid for anyone presenting yoga to pre-school children. Often the asanas are drawn as stick figures. These are done by the teacher one bit at a time, allowing the children to copy each part either into their own notebooks or onto the blackboards.
- *Rhythm instruments* are very easy to make and are essential auditory tools. Music and rhythm are very important methods for developing auditory attention in children.

The session

What is involved in a yoga session with children of this age? It is customary when conducting a yoga class, or when doing one's own practice, to begin with the physical postures, then breathing exercises, then relaxation, concentration or meditation. This same structure is used for pre-school children, so let us look at each of these three parts individually.

Yoga zoo

As previously stated, many postures normally done with children of this age often have the names of animals. Sometimes they are trying to assume the position of that animal, while relaxing, while moving and so on. With children of pre-school age these postures are presented as our 'yoga zoo'. With the children we pretend to go to the yoga zoo and at the zoo we see a lion, a tiger, a duck, rabbit, etc. One can also go on a safari into the jungle or any place where one might meet any of these animals.

This form of play is used to include vocabulary for the child. We can go to the 'aviary' to see the crow, the stork, the swan, or to the 'reptile' house to see the cobra. The butterfly can be seen flying from a rose to a lily. The children are encouraged to suggest a flower that the butterfly is going to land on next; or it may fly from a pink rose, to a white rose, to a red rose, a yellow rose, to roses of all colours.

P. Levenstein (1973) in her paper, 'Cognitive Development Through Verbalized Play', argues that a child's intellectual development is closely linked to his verbal growth and his cognitive development can be influenced by the amount and quality of verbal interaction between child and mother. This holds true as well for teachers, playgroup leaders and yoga teachers. Levenstein is supported in this argument by other researchers like Bruner and Deutch, who maintain that intellectual development linked to later academic success seems to be closely tied to the child's verbal development occurring between twenty months and four years.

Make believe play is at its height between the ages of about eighteen months and seven or eight years. This coincides with learning to refer to objects in their absence, and with communication by means of language or symbolic gestures. As the child develops during this period, he makes enormous strides in his ability to 'communicate' to self and others, broadly speaking, and to assimilate and use communications from others. The teacher should use his own imagination to make the asanas exciting and informative for the young child. For example, while visiting the lion we see he has his tongue hanging out. He is feeling very hot so he is cooling himself. What other animals hang their tongues out to cool themselves? Does your dog do it? In this way the yoga teacher can introduce ideas, knowledge, all sorts of information while making believe with the child.

The blossoming lotus

The children should sit in a circle with their feet pointing towards the centre, holding hands. They then bring their heads down towards their knees and their hands towards the feet, as in paschimottanasana, still holding hands. They are told that the flower is sleeping because it is night time and as the sun comes up over the horizon the flower slowly starts to wake up. First they raise their body back to the sitting position, then slowly raise their arms above their heads. Still holding hands they slowly lie down on the floor. They then raise one leg very slowly, followed by the other leg, then finally bring them both down to the floor behind the head, in halasana. The flower is then fully opened. When it is evening, the flower will slowly close and go to sleep again.

The tree

The children can begin this from a squatting position. The tree is just a small seed planted in the ground. The rain comes and brings water to the seed. Then the sun comes out and the light causes the seed to send roots down into the ground and shoots above the ground. As the tree grows the children first stand, then stretch up onto tiptoes with their arms stretched high above their heads with fingers spread wide apart as they become full-grown.

The bridge

While some children are being a bridge, others can be fish or alligators or anything that the child imagines is swimming under the bridge.

Teapot pose

In this posture the child balances on the left leg, while holding the right ankle with the right hand. The left elbow is bent and resting against the body and the left hand is sticking out, with the fingers pointing away from the body at about shoulder height. Slowly bend forward, causing the right foot and the knee to come up behind the back, maintaining balance at the same time.

Children can learn to sing while practising this posture:

I'm a little teapot, short and stout,
Here is my handle, (right arm)
Here is my spout. (left hand)
When the tea is ready hear me shout,
Tip me over and pour me out. (bend forward)

I have found that young children who start such postures at about three years of age, often by about age five can be observed combining different postures in their own 'dance'. You can see how they carefully experiment with the movement out of one posture flowing into the next. This indicates a tremendous development in body awareness and creative thinking.

Bhramari pranayama (humming bee breath)

The easiest breathing technique to teach children of this age is bhramari pranayama, the humming bee breath. When small children are asked to breathe in deeply they tend to inhale very noisily but very shallowly. To encourage deep inhalation the child has to be made aware of doing long, slow exhalation first. In bhramari they are asked to hum out as long as possible with one breath, listening to the sound all the time. This encourages deep inhalation after having practised a few times, as well as developing concentration and listening.

The children readily join in this practice because they love making sounds. Quite often in a playgroup, one child will start to hum or maybe even repeat a word again and again. This is usually taken up by the others present and becomes a sort of chant. So the humming bee breath is readily practised by children of this age.

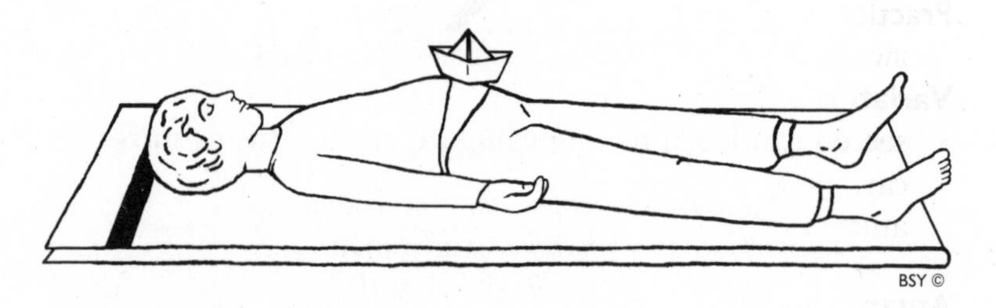

Abdominal breathing

To encourage abdominal breathing, ask the child to lie down on the floor. Place a small paper boat, which the child has made previously, at the navel. Explain that when he breathes in, a wave is created by the stomach as it swells out; when he breathes out the wave subsides. By being able to watch the boat on the waves, the child develops awareness of the abdomen and abdominal breathing which he normally does unconsciously.

RELAXATION, VISUALIZATION AND CREATIVE ATTENTION

Yoga nidra

A child of this age cannot be expected to stay still for a very long time. Yoga nidra is a very powerful form of relaxation, though relaxation is only a by-product of the technique. Two important parts of the technique are rotation of awareness, that is, developing awareness of the physical body, and creative visualization. Practices like yoga nidra have to be modified for children of this age. Instead of asking young children to feel a body part without moving it, they are asked to practise it in the following way:

Technique

First be a statue without moving until I count to 10. Bend your elbows, now make them straight. Bend your knees, straighten them again. Wriggle your toes, make them still. Raise your head, lower it. Move the eyeballs with your eyes closed, now stop. Move the lips as if to whistle, relax them.

Practice note: This practice helps children to localize their awareness in the different body parts.

Variation: The children can imagine their own front door, see the colour and all the details, see their pet, the family car, their own shoes, etc. Or one can combine it with antar mouna, listening.

Antar mouna

Antar mouna is a technique for learning to make the mind quiet and receptive. At a certain stage in the practice the practitioner is asked to be completely aware of all external experiences. This part of antar mouna can also be used very successfully with children of this age. However, instead of just being asked to listen to all the sounds, the child is asked to listen while the teacher points out all the sounds within the environment. He may say, "Hear the bird singing. Hear the bus moving down the street. Which way is it travelling?

How many different sounds can you hear? How many different sounds can you hear at the same time? Locate where the sound is coming from."

Kirtan

Kirtan is a method of using sound for focusing attention and developing aural perceptions, as well as expressing emotions. Sounds are produced by the person, either with his voice in singing or chanting, or with his hands or feet in keeping rhythm, or by using all of them, as we have previously said.

Rhythm instruments may also be used for kirtan. Singing and using rhythm instruments are also very important forms of yoga to do with children of this age. This helps to develop auditory attention which is very important for later learning, especially for learning to read. Kirtans are so simple that even the youngest child can sing them. They are not too concerned with what the song means but quite willingly join in.

There are many children's songs that occur in more than one language. They are simply fun and the children love to sing them in many languages. One example is:

Are you sleeping? Are you sleeping?
Brother John, Brother John
Morning bells are ringing, morning bells are ringing,
Ding, dang, dong; ding, dang, dong.

Bruder Jacob, Bruder Jacob,
Schlaefst Du noch? Schlaefst Du noch?
Es laeuten schon die Glocken,
Es laeuten schon die Glocken,
Bim, bam, bong; bim, bam, bong.

Frere Jacques, Frere Jacques,
Dormez vous? Dormez vous?
Sonnent les Matines, Sonnent les Matines,
Ding, dang, dong; ding, dang, dong.

15

Yoga Techniques for 7–14 Year-Olds

Arundhati & Swami Yogabhakti Saraswati

Yoga classes for children should be presented differently from classes designed for adults. The asanas should be presented more as dynamic rather than static postures and perfection of the asanas is not demanded with children. This will come with practice. Any of the asanas or pranayamas described in chapters 16 to 31 may be used for classes with children of this age group. The teacher should use imagination to make these practices interesting and varied for the children.

Below are a few suggestions for asanas, games, pranayama and relaxation to use with children of this age. It is a good idea to work with the children sitting in a circle. This helps them develop a feeling of group participation since none have their backs to any other children. Yoga and modern dance have been successfully used with this age group. The body awareness that is developed through the yoga postures is used in expressing concrete or abstract ideas by the dance movements.

Blossoming lotus

Sit with feet pointed towards the centre and assume paschimottanasana.

Slowly sit up, trying to keep in rhythm with the person on either side. Arms are stretched high above the head.

Gradually lower the back, then the head, down to the floor, bringing the arms to the floor by the sides. (Later the arms may be brought to the floor, still outstretched over the head.) Raise the right leg until the foot is above the navel, then raise the left leg bringing the feet together. Then, lowering the feet towards the head, lift the hips up off the floor. Straighten the legs back up in the air into sarvangasana, supporting the waist with the hands if necessary.

Slowly lower the right toes to the floor behind the head. Then lower the left toes and place them beside the right ones, assuming halasana. Now the flower has bloomed completely.

Practice note: This differs from the exercise described in the previous chapter in that the children are not holding hands. It may be practised in both ways.

Any children who are unable to participate in these asanas can be the stamen of the lotus and stand at the centre of the flower with arms upstretched in tadasana.

The blossoming lotus is a very beautiful asana when done with a large group of children so that one has smaller circles within circles.

Variation 1: While in halasana take tiny side steps and walk as far to the right as possible, then return walking to the centre behind the head. Then walk as far to the left as possible, returning back to centre.

This variation is also known as the twisting lotus.

Benefits: This variation brings in a very important movement for the spine. It also provides the benefits of the twisting asanas.

Variation 2: From halasana bring the right arm slowly up over the head and take hold of the right ankle. Bring the left arm up and take hold of the left ankle. Slowly open the legs as wide as possible, continuing to hold the ankles. Try to bring the foot and hand close to the foot and hand of the people on the other side, then bring the feet back together.

Variation 3: From halasana bend the knees and try to place them on the floor beside the right ear. Straighten the legs again. Then bend the knees and bring them to the floor near the left ear and straighten them. Again bend the knees and bring the right knee beside the right ear and the left knee beside the left ear. Then bring the arms up and wrap them around the thighs, as in pashinee mudra.

Surya Namaskara (salutations to the sun)

Surya namaskara is described in chapter 20. Stress the mental counting of 1 to 12 while teaching the asanas so that the children start to subvocalize the numbers.

Chandra Namaskara (salutations to the moon)

There are three different sequences in this practice, all are fully described in chapter 21.

Warrior sequence

The warrior sequence has three levels of practice. The first level is easy and the two following levels increase in difficulty. This sequence is well described in chapter 22.

Asanas done in pairs

Wheelbarrow, stambhanasana, dancing duo, see-saw, the double windmill, and the chinese dragon are just some of many asanas that children can do together. Building pyramids is also a very enjoyable way to do asanas and it involves several children at one time.

Animal spirits

The ancient rishis of India devised a number of asanas based on their patient observations of nature. Earth, ocean and sky, sun and space, and all that could be seen or heard through common experience were contemplated by the sages who had a wealth of knowledge about human life. It is not by chance that a whole jungle of animal postures is known in hatha yoga terminology. Each posture or pose, whether the lion, camel, cat or peacock, has a meaning of its own.

Underlying all these is a warning from Mother Nature that we are born of her, and that no mastery is possible until the animal in us has been fully recognized and accepted. Only then can it be conquered, not by force, but through a process of maturation. We call it 'growth', and this is what the course of human life is showing us. It is natural for children to live the first stage of their evolution with joy and enthusiasm. Let them love the movements of animals, the sounds of the beasts and birds, and the rustling of the wind through the trees.

Being trees

It is difficult for young children to stand on only one foot, since the mechanism for equilibrium is slow to develop. Why not train it the best possible way? One of the asanas that can help develop balance is eka pada pranamasana, which children from six to eleven will enjoy doing.

The children stand in a circle or in line. There should be enough space between them so that they will not touch each other when they raise one foot in the way that suits them best. Don't insist on the correct arrangement of legs and feet as is taught in the yoga manuals. In time the children will learn. First let them learn how to manage their balance somehow, while moving their trunk and arms.

Once they have understood and tried the process, you may tell them, "Now lift your right leg and place your right foot on top of the left foot, or just a bit above the floor, as you like. Now slowly raise your arms sideways, as if they were big branches spreading under the sky. Your fingers are the smaller twigs and branches, and your hairs are the leaves. Hear the leaves rustling in the gentle breeze as the wind is passing by, you are swayed to and fro. See if you can close your eyes. (Most will lose their balance in doing so; they have to learn that too!) You are little trees growing in the forest. When you feel tired you can change legs. Now the wind has stopped blowing, you are motionless, calm and happy. Gently bring down your foot and lower your arms."

Children will imbibe a lot from this game, as they will be made to feel how closely they are related to the world of plants. Our kinship with trees has often been emphasized in various scriptures, and the pleasure that children derive from playing 'trees' proves this to be a deep instinct in the human race. It will also make them aware of their upright position in space and will develop their balance on the physical as well as the emotional plane. By observing their change of feeling when they close their eyes, older children will realize the importance of concentrating their gaze on one single point while doing this posture.

Watch the cat

The children should sit on their knees and then bend forward in marjariasana, the 'cat pose', stretching their arms and meowing. Then they should silently relax sideways, as cats often do when basking in the sun, lying completely limp as if they were empty bundles of fur, but even then remaining fully aware of what is going on around them.

If a cat hears a meaningful noise, immediately it will spring onto its feet. So while the children are relaxing fully on the floor, keep on speaking to them: "Now you are lying down as if you were asleep, but you are not. You are vigilant cats, even though you look like sleeping cats, and you are listening attentively to me. As soon as I say the word 'mouse' (or any other word or sound you choose), you will spring into the stretching cat pose again in a flash. For the moment you are doing nothing; feel your body, breath going in and out of your nose..."

Keep on giving them instructions on how to relax in the right way until in the course of your talking, without any warning, you mention the word 'mouse' (or any other). This will immediately bring the children onto their knees again. This game is a favourite with children from five to twelve years. Children will learn the meaning of awareness from such games. They will be made to feel that relaxation can be allied with vigilance.

The wise cat and the proud lion

Yogic games can be followed by suitable stories adapted for children which enlarge upon the practices already learned. This is an excellent way to inculcate spiritual truths without boredom or disinterest arising. Take, for example, the story of the wise cat.

The cat is a great guru indeed, as the following story will show. Long ago, in the times when the animals spoke, the cat was regarded as the wisest creature of all. Some cats even displayed such intelligence and capacities that their fellow animals came long distances to learn from them. Once there was a cat who was considered to be a great master, so much so that even fish would swim the oceans and rivers to his abode, and cows and monkeys would travel for months to be taught by him. Even kingly eagles would leave their snow-capped mountain peaks to ask his advice. The wise cat was living a simple life in the forest, and the animals who came to be his pupils served him with love and reverence.

A lion once happened to knock at the door of the cat's house and said, "I have come from my native jungle to learn from you. Please, teach me so that I can improve. I will listen to you in every way." The cat accepted and taught him how to spring, to hunt and to roar loudly. He showed the lion how to fight with courage, sniff his prey from afar, run swiftly over hills and through valleys, and see in the dark on moonless nights. The lion lived peacefully within the community and learned how to feed sparingly when there was not enough to eat, and to share it in times of plenty.

So he thought he had become wise in his turn, but he had also developed great pride because he was the strongest and most fearless of animals. He said to himself, "Now the cat has transmitted all his knowledge to me and I have come to know as much as he. I am also bigger and stronger than he. I am tired of listening to him, I will now take his place." Once, as the cat was sleeping all by himself under a big oak tree, the lion pounced on him to swallow him up. But the cat had sensed his presence, for he was not fully asleep, and was able to jump onto the highest branch of the tree. Although the lion, wild with rage, tried to catch him, it was no use.

The cat spoke to him from the top of the tree: "Don't think that you have learned everything from me. I still know more. Now go away from here and be content to remain what you are." And since that time the lion and the cat have parted ways.

BREATHING AND RELAXATION PRACTICES

Pranayama

Any breathing practices from chapters 16 and 29 will be fun and very useful for the children. Some examples are, the punctured balloon, or the deflated tyre, the Tibetan purification exercise and many others. The importance of pranayama for children cannot be overstated. Emotional stability comes about more easily for children who regularly practise breathing techniques.

Relaxation is also for children

Can we balance our children through relaxation? Some teachers have tried it. Knowing that a child's capacity for listening is closely related to his physical and emotional state and that restlessness grows year by year among students, these teachers are practising a few easy relaxation exercises.

The results of this foresight is that their pupils learn and express themselves much more easily. If the children do not have this opportunity at school, you can teach them to relax even without ever having practised these exercises yourself. However, experience makes the best teachers. Only take care to adjust the instructions to the level of the child and do not force him to focus his attention for more than 10 minutes. Here are four exercises all inspired by yoga. Each exercise has a particular quality.

Concentration without effort

The first is a famous exercise which has been adopted by countless American businessmen. Elbows are on the table, hands cupped over the closed eyes. Breathe in deeply, and slowly breathe out. Practise twelve times. Evoke in the child a landscape or place that he likes. Let him imagine that he is there, at one with trees, mountains, sea or sky.

Attention and imagination

Place an object or picture in front of the child. Eyes are motionless but without tension. Let him look at the object for 30 seconds. Then, with closed eyes, encourage him to see the object clearly. Then, for a second time, let him look at the object in detail with open eyes.

Inner peace of mind

This exercise is based on listening to sounds. While the child is lying, or better, sitting with the back straight and eyes closed, ask him/her to breathe six times, repeating mentally either the word 'peace' or 'relaxation' at the end of each breath. Then, make him/her listen to the noises, first in the distance, in the street, then in the room, but without trying to interpret them. A different way to practise with smaller children is for the teacher to produce three different sounds, for example, those of crumpled paper, a click of a ballpen and the sound of a step (when someone walks). Then ask them in which order the sounds were produced.

Relaxation without sleeping (yoga nidra)

With the child lying down, name the different parts of the body which he has to feel without moving. Start with the thumb of the right hand, move up the arm and then down the right side to the toes. Practise the same way for the left side of the body. Finish with the head. Then suggest visualization of pleasant pictures to imagine. See chapter 16 on yoga techniques in the classroom for ideas about how to structure yoga nidra for children of this age.

16

Yoga Techniques for the Classroom

Swami Yogabhakti Saraswati

The techniques described in this chapter are for use in a normal school classroom, even those with fixed desks and seats. Most of the exercises can be done while standing and moving between the desks, others can even be done while sitting at the desk.

Limbering up and developing body awareness

The following exercises are described in chapter 18. In the classroom it is not even necessary for the children to remove their shoes in order to perform them.

1. Ankle bending (5 times).
2. Ankle rotation (5 times clockwise then 5 times anti-clockwise). Either both together or one at a time, depending upon the time available.
3. Knee bending (5 times each leg).
4. Squat and rise pose (5 times).
5. Hand clenching (5 times).
6. Wrist bending (5 times).
7. Wrist rotation (5 times clockwise/anti-clockwise). Each wrist individually or both together.
8. Elbow bending (5 times). Slow inhalation as arm is extended, slow exhalation as elbow is bent.
9. Shoulder rotations (5 times clockwise/anti-clockwise).
10. Neck movements (5 times) each variation.
11. Eye movements.
12. Palming.

All these exercises lend themselves well to synchronization of the breath. When being used in a language classroom, for example, these exercises are often practised in rhythm to a popular tune of that language, which the children can all respond to readily.

Tibetan purification exercise

This is also called the *Ha Ha* exercise. It is a breathing and cleansing exercise that gives an outlet for children's agitation when they want to shout and you cannot silence them. Suppose they are coming in from outside and are very excited. If the teacher tells them to shout, they will be very pleased and you will later be able to discipline their animal spirits.

Technique

Stand with the hands resting against the sides of the body at the level of the floating ribs, at about waist level. As you are breathing in feel the lower ribs expanding. While breathing out, press gently with the hands. Inhale slowly, and exhale while gently bending forward a little at the waist. This helps expel the air.

Now bring the hands up level with the middle of the ribcage. Inhale, expand the chest, and press gently while exhaling, bending forward slightly more.

Place the palms of the hands on the upper part of the chest near the shoulders. Inhale and press gently while exhaling, at the same time bending forward slightly.

Now practise all three together. Inhale with the hands moving quickly on either side of the ribcage. Exhale by shouting "Ha", simultaneously bending slightly forward and pressing; another "Ha" bending further and pressing; and again "Ha", letting the hands drop down and the head remains down. This is very good for the brain.

Then inhale slowly, starting with the head down, raise the body upright and repeat the Ha... Ha... Ha... exercise again, dropping the hands and head down at the end.

Watch the faces of the children and you will observe that the eyes are brighter and the children are more relaxed from releasing tension through the shouting and breathing.

Making a mandala

This is a group practice. A mandala is a collection of geometrical patterns. Here we make a large circle or maybe a circle within a circle, depending upon the number of children involved. In yoga, colours and shapes are very important for influencing the deeper levels of the child's mind.

Technique

Stand in a circle, with the left palm facing the ceiling and the right palm facing the floor so that the hands are joined with the next person. First we create an atmosphere in the group. Then we will create a link through breathing. Inhale through the left palm, then exhale through the right palm. Feel that a current is passing through the hands and around the circle. Close the eyes and go on inhaling through the left palm and exhaling through the right. It is like electricity passing from left to right. Then relax the arms and release the hands of your neighbours.

Becoming statues: STOP exercise

This practice aims to create a lively atmosphere where children can learn about movement and motionlessness. It is important to create a lively atmosphere for children, so that they feel it is good to be alive and it is pleasant to be at school, or to be together in a group. This is a classic yoga exercise. Sometimes the master said to the disciples, "STOP! Stop whatever you are doing!" So they had to stop whatever they were doing, whether cutting wood, sweeping the floor, or reading a manuscript.

The idea of this exercise is to make one realize: "What am I doing? Who am I? Where am I? Where is my awareness?" These STOP exercises are greatly enjoyed by children and are called 'becoming statues'.

Technique

Stage 1: Just walk and move about randomly, bringing your attention to the different parts of the body as they are named. When you hear '*STOP*' shouted loudly, then stop and bring the attention to whatever is asked of you.

- Move about randomly and feel the soles of your feet,
- Feel your back but keep on walking and moving about,
- Feel the tip of your nose,
- Chest,
- Knees, keep moving,
- Right hand,
- Feel your navel.
- STOP! Do not move your eyes, fingers, hair or anything.

Stage 2: Start to move around again but move more quickly; do not touch anyone else. Take great care not to touch anyone.

- Move backwards without touching anyone.
- Move sideways without touching anyone.
- STOP!

Potato stop

This practice aims to balance awareness between motion and motionlessness. There is a little rhyme in English which you may well remember: *One potato, two potato, three potato, four.* Other rhymes in other languages may be used for teaching purposes as well as for releasing tensions. One may use the word 'banana' or any other favourite word as long as it has three syllables.

Technique

Stage 1: While shouting each line of the above rhyme, move about making big strides and bending the knees in turn, stretching the legs as far as possible so that the steps are very big, and large amounts of space are covered. 'Four' means STOP, but stop is not shouted out.
Take another stride so that you are facing the person closest to you. Say, "Oh, you are here, how come?", and start a conversation with that person.

Stage 2: Repeat the movement, this time moving more quietly and whispering the rhyme. After 'Four' turn to the person nearby and pay him or her a compliment.

Stage 3: Repeat the movement but this time only repeat the rhyme mentally. After 'Four' turn to the person nearby and look at him or her very closely. Then close your eyes and try to remember that person's face. Open your eyes and check your memory. Close your eyes again and try to remember again. Then open your eyes.

Ostrich pose

This practice aims to to correct spinal defects. It is also used to develop balance, attention and concentration. As a dynamic pose it is the ostrich running around, releasing tensions.

Technique

Form a circle.
Do the ostrich pose (see page 216 for instructions).
Exhale, then inhale and come upright again.

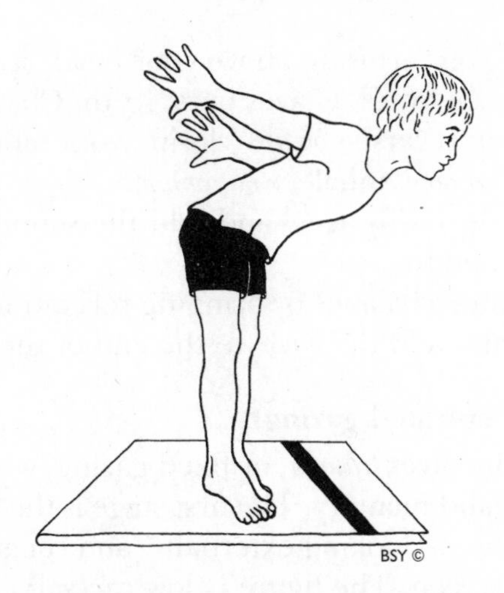

Exhale, then do the ostrich again.

Inhale, move to a vertical position and rise up on the toes, then exhale and move to the horizontal position of the ostrich.

Repeat several times. Then start to move around the circle in the ostrich posture, walking then gradually increasing the speed until the ostrich is running.

The growing tree

In learning to breathe we notice that breathing takes place on three different levels. We will use sound to locate these, and try to feel the relaxation from chanting the sounds. We will also make movements like a growing tree. The tree is like a child, first it is very small, then it gets bigger, then makes branches and leaves spreading towards the sky.

Technique

First level of sound is *aa* as in car. Second level is *oo* as in door. Third level is *ee* as in tree.

Let your arms hang down by your sides and you will breathe better in the abdomen. Chant car or *aa*.

Now put the arms, elbow to elbow close by in front of your chest. Chant door or *oo*.

Then raise your arms up above your head, spreading the fingers like the trees. Leaves burst forth. Chant *tree* or *ee*. Now chant in reverse *e oo am* (closing your mouth). Inhale and repeat, *a oo e*, inhale, *e oo ammm*.
Repeat 'the growing tree' and add the sounds following your own rhythm.
Mmmm creates a balance by bringing relaxation. To create energy do not add the *mmm* to the end of the vowel.

Trataka (concentrated gazing)
This exercise involves *trataka*, or fixed gazing, which devlops concentration and memory. The first stage is the wide screen with the eyes open, looking externally, and the second level is the mental screen. The figure below can serve as a model for objects to be used in this exercise.

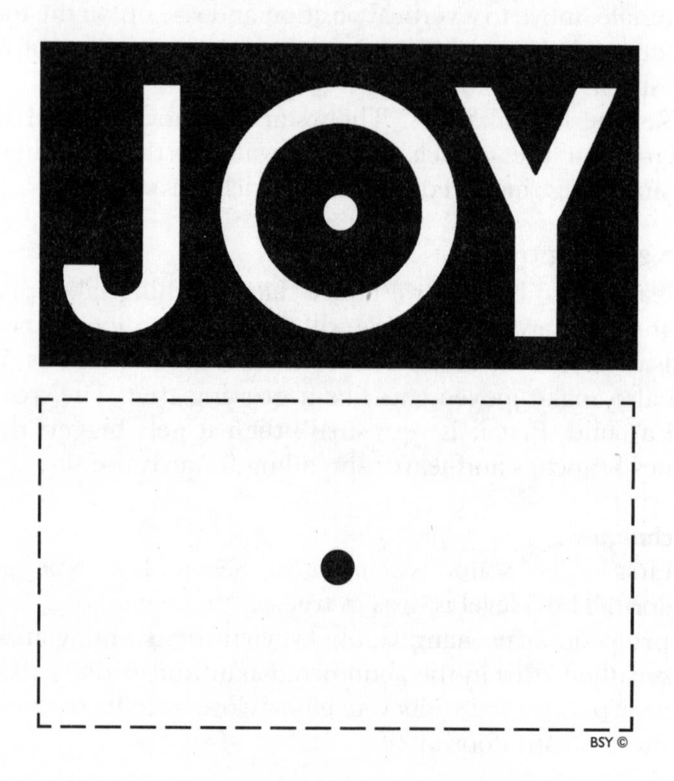

Technique

Stage 1: Hold the paper card out in front of you, about an arm's length away at eye level.
Practise trataka (fixed gazing) on the little point in the middle of the word on the paper.
Look at the word on the paper card.
Look at it, and do not move for 60 seconds.
Fix the gaze on the central point.

Stage 2: Now close your eyes for a second.
Then open them and look at the dot below the word on the paper.
The counter-image will come and go.
It is an optical process; there is nothing magic about it.
Repeat it again. Look at the dot.
Close your eyes.
Now look at the dot below the word on the paper.
Again close the eyes.
Put the paper down.
Keep the eyes closed and see what happens.

Stage 3: Now sing *om* together.
Inhale but keep looking inside at the point.
Om, om, om.
Now finish the practice and open your eyes.

Stop and write

This practice aids in developing the sense of touch. Assume it is that time of day when we want to wake up a bit, to feel full of energy. So we are going to write and do important things but we will use our backs for that, like a blackboard.

Technique

Stage 1: Just walk around anywhere and after a while I will stay STOP. Today you will walk around while imitating a profession, for example, like typewriting, painting and so on. One of these is your profession and while walking around you will mime it. So walk around, showing that you are a professional.

Stage 2: STOP. Now tell your friend next to you what you are doing and talk about your job.

Stage 3: STOP. Now one of the two partners turns his back to the other. The back is like a blackboard but it has to be wiped clean. So rub the board clean. (This is a very nice way of massaging your friend's back.)
Next you will write. It is an exercise in tactile attention. With your finger, write a letter on the back (blackboard) and the other person will sing the letters. Do not forget to wipe the board clean in between writing the letters.

Stage 4: STOP. Now change roles. Whoever was previously the blackboard should write a few letters on the other person's back.

Benefits: This exercise leaves the children feeling very active and very much alive.

Chanting vowels

This practice aims to develop touch awareness and relaxation.

Technique

While chanting a vowel place your hands on your head, then on the ribcage, back, abdomen, chest, throat and so on to perceive the parts of the body where the vowel sounds are resounding most.
Chant each vowel in this way.

Om mantra merry-go-round

This practice aids in developing concentration and group awareness.

Technique

Form three circles. The outer, larger circle will move clockwise and chant the sound *aaa*. The middle circle will move anti-clockwise while chanting *uuu*. The small, inner circle will move clockwise chanting *mmm*. Then gently slow down and stop the movement, but continue chanting for a while.

Correlating asanas and sound

This practice aims to develop the child's attention and memory. Children must learn yoga for their own well-being. Here we have devised an exercise in which we combine hatha and nada yoga for the development of attention and memory.

Technique

Stage 1: Here we will practise the asanas and sounds together: Do tadasana which will be associated with the sound *aaa*. Close the eyes and listen to the *aaa* sound and visualize the pose.

Stage 2: Do the second posture, *eka pada pranamasana*, the tree pose. Stand on one leg as a tree. This posture will be associated with *ee* as in bee. Close the eyes, hear the sound *ee*, and visualize the pose.

Stage 3: Do the third posture, *garudasana*, the eagle. It is associated with the sound *oo*, as in good. Now close the eyes, hear *oo* and visualize the eagle with *oo*.

Stage 4: Do the fourth posture, *dolasana*, the pendulum pose. It is associated with the sound *o*, as in bow. Close the eyes, hear the *o* sound and visualize the pose.

Now move around and when I call out one of the sounds, do the pose associated with this sound. Walk around quickly and the stop signal will be the vowel sounds: *ee*, *o*, *oo*, *o*, *aa*, *ee*, *oo*, *ee*, *aa*, etc.

Sitting at a desk

This practice aids in straightening the back. We are going to do an exercise which can be done while sitting on a chair. In classrooms one has to pick out the exercises that can be done either sitting on chairs at a desk, or standing between tables and chairs.

Children usually say that it hurts. When I tell them, "In that case we will not do it", they protest and say they will do it. I remind them that it hurts, and they say, "Yes, but it does us good". So we all laugh together.

Technique

Stage 1: Sit upright, now lean slightly forward, placing the fists on either side of the neck, just below the ears. If at a desk, the chest can rest lightly on the desk.

Imagine that the head is winning and is pulling the fists with it. (Use the head to push backwards.)

Then imagine that the fists are winning and pushing the head forward. (Use the fists to pull the head forwards.)

Now imagine that the fists are pushing but the head resists.

Then make little wings with the elbows. Push the shoulder blades back together as much as possible and smile.

Stage 2: Then inhale and sit upright as straight as possible, as straight as an umbrella.

Exhale and push the head forward, but do not touch the table with your head, only the chest should be touching.

Stage 3: Inhale, sit upright, keep the shoulders up.

Exhale forcefully and drop your head forward. Then lower your arms.

The punctured balloon

The following practices aid in relaxing the back.

Technique

Either sitting or standing, keep the legs slightly apart.

As you inhale through the nostrils, imagine that you are a big balloon or a big tyre that is being filled up with air, cheeks and all, while I am blowing. (This is done rhythmically in 3 or 4 puffs.)

Then, unfortunately there is a puncture.

Breathing out through the mouth, *psst* the air goes out, as you drop the upper body forward and down.

Variation: Imagine that you are completely exhausted. Your back is bent and I am going to pump air into you so that you feel really full of pep.

Exhale, then inhale – pump, pump, pump, pump, pump.

Straighten up slightly with each pump.

Exhale through the mouth.

And the back is bent once more.
This time we will do the reverse process.
We inhale continuously, and straighten up smoothly to an upright sitting posture.
And exhale in spurts: *ha-ha-ha-ha-ha*.
Lowering more and more with each spurt.
Then inhale and feel you are refreshed.

Breathing with pictures

These techniques aim to develop imagination and correct breathing. Here we are using types of breathing which are classical techniques in yoga. Children are fond of images, so in this practice we use pictures and imagination to assist in the performance of breathing. Imagine how you would teach breathing to children. First a child has to learn that he breathes and these techniques are designed to make him aware of it. Some children may be anxious about silence, closing their eyes and relaxing. When you try it you will see that some children do not like it. They are afraid, so do not think all children will like silence as adults do.

You can teach breathing by letting children look at a picture. Use anything to summon the awareness of the breathing process. They may use the fingers to trace the outline because children need something concrete to do. Their minds are not yet totally abstract. They want to look, feel, touch, see and smell. There are ways to help children become aware of their breath, as instructed in the following techniques:

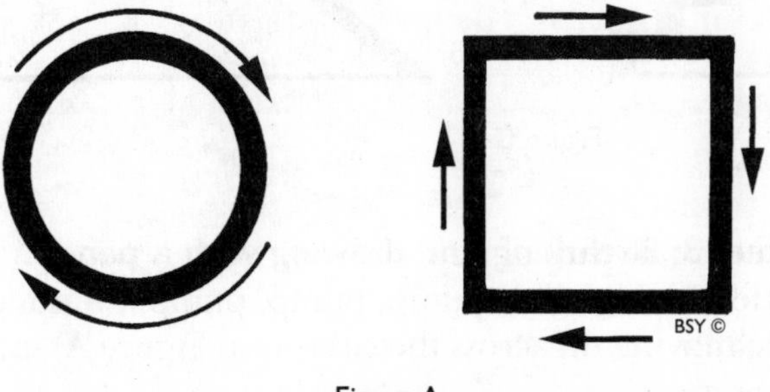

Figure A

Technique 1: Breathing with a circle or square

Breathing is like a circle.
Inhale and exhale around the circle, inhaling half way around, then exhaling and completing the circle.
(You may also use a square; see Figure A.)

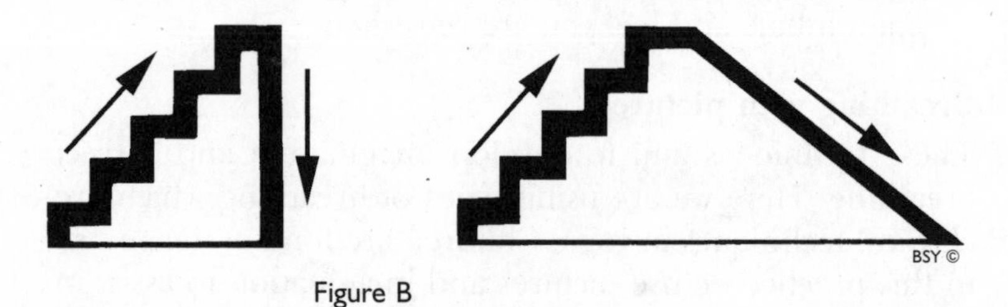

Figure B

Technique 2: Breathing with a staircase

Look at the figures (see Figure B).
First we have a picture of a staircase.
Inhale while ascending the stairs.
Exhale descending the lift, or on the banister.
We can also reverse this technique (see Figure C)
Inhale while ascending in a lift or escalator.
Exhale while descending the stairs.

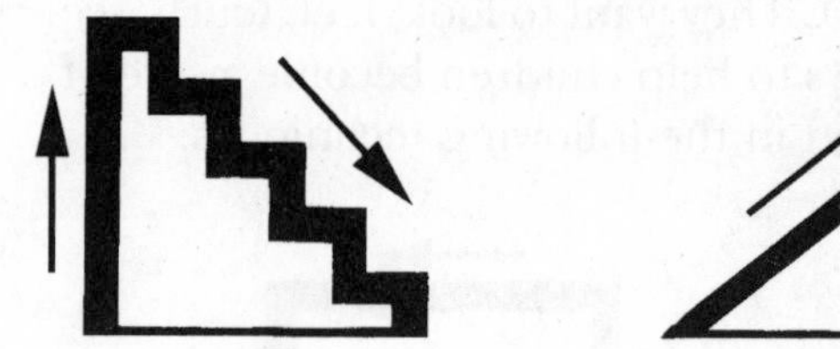

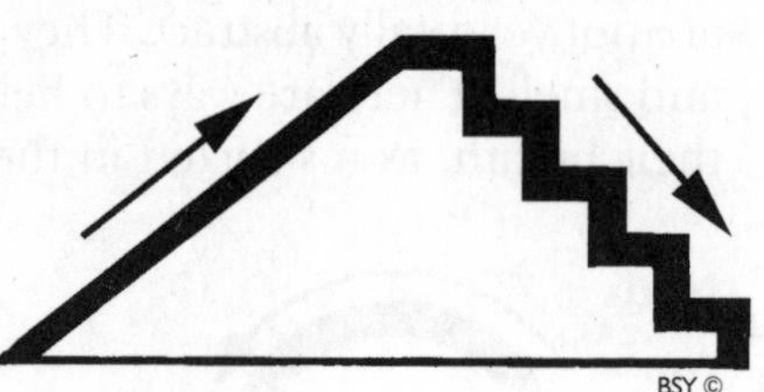

Figure C

Technique 3: Breathing and drawing with a pencil
Stage 1: Drawing circles

While moving up across the circle (see Figure A) say "I am inhaling".

While moving down under the circle, say "I am exhaling, I know it".

Practice note: After a little while the children can be made to realize that there is a break between inhaling and exhaling. Just like a wave, when the sea rises and falls, there is a moment when there is no movement. The same thing is happening with breathing. It is like a big wave.

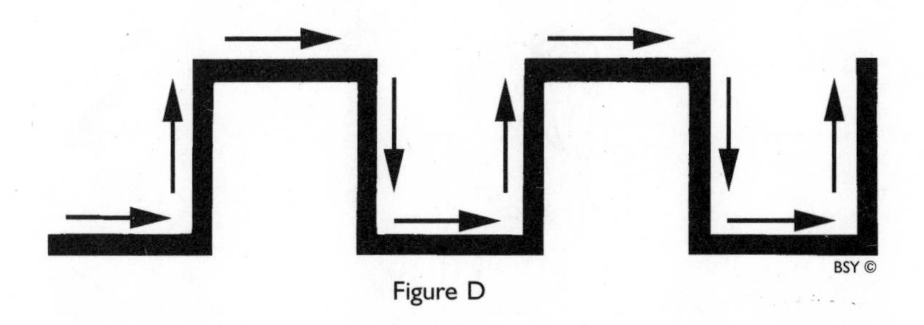

Figure D

Stage 2: Drawing castles

Then you repeat the breathing and drawing, with William the Conqueror's castle (see above Figure D).

Inhale, stop! Exhale, stop! Inhale, stop! Exhale, stop!

Practice note: Imagining being a castle shape is actually very interesting for children and they can actually draw it while breathing. With pen in hand, they draw it while breathing in, then stop. While exhaling they draw and stop. This is also a way to breathe regularly while doing something.

Nadi shodhana using hands, arms or legs

Among all the types of respiration techniques there is one that is most precious. It is called *nadi shodhana*, or alternate nostril breathing, which creates a balance between the ida and pingala nadis and also maintains the pineal gland in good condition. Research has shown that it is absolutely essential for children to practise exercises where both sides of the brain are stimulated. Nadi shodhana is an excellent technique for this.

I should say it would be excellent but it is so difficult and boring for the children. Besides there is a problem. Very often you will find in class that half the children will not do it because one of their nostrils is blocked by a cold or something else. So we must find another way of doing alternate breathing. We have found a few exercises to do this without the inconvenience of the nostrils being alternately closed and opened.

Technique

Sit with the hands on the knees and practise alternate breathing using the fingers.

Raise the right index finger while inhaling, exhale while lowering the left index finger.

Inhale, raise left index finger, exhale, lower right index finger. Continue in this way.

Variation 1: You can also use all the fingers alternately. It becomes more complex but demands more concentration and attention. .

Variation 2: It can also be done while sitting and raising the arms alternately instead of raising the fingers. Find other ways to vary this same exercise

Variation 3: The same practice can be done using legs as well. Lie down in *makarasana*, the crocodile pose.

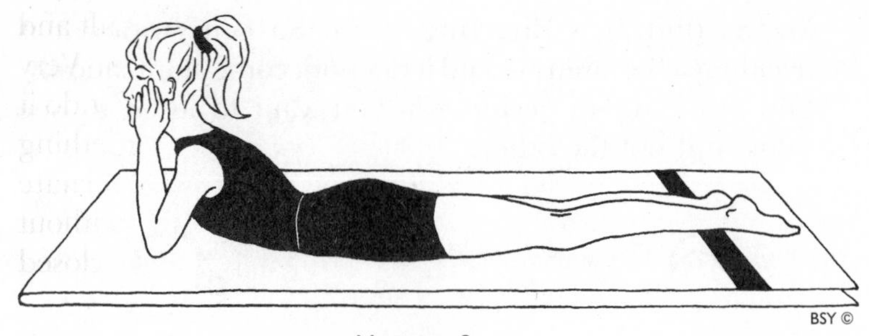

Variation 3

Breathe in and bend the right leg up, slowly put the foot back down with exhalation.

Breathe in, bend the left leg, breathe out and slowly put the foot back down.

Practice note: This is a little game between the two feet, an interplay between the legs and the breath. While the children are doing this, they can also listen to some music.

Directing attention

This practice aims to develop concentration and direct attention. Two readers are chosen to stand on either side of the class to read different stories simultaneously. It is decided to listen only to the story from the reader standing on the right side. So first the students should rub the right ear, massage it slightly, pulling it up, down and sideways; making sure that they can hear, then continue with the following instructions:

Technique

Stage 1: Listen to the reader on the right. (Allow the stories to be read for a few minutes.) STOP.

Stage 2: Now they should rub the other ear but continue to concentrate on the story from the reader on the right. STOP.

Practice note: As said in the scriptures, the horses are being led by the charioteer. The mind (the charioteer) decides what it is going to imbibe from the senses (the horses).

Manas (mind) is directing it all. So concentration is deciding to be attentive and it does not come automatically. You also have to decide that you want to listen to one thing and not the other.

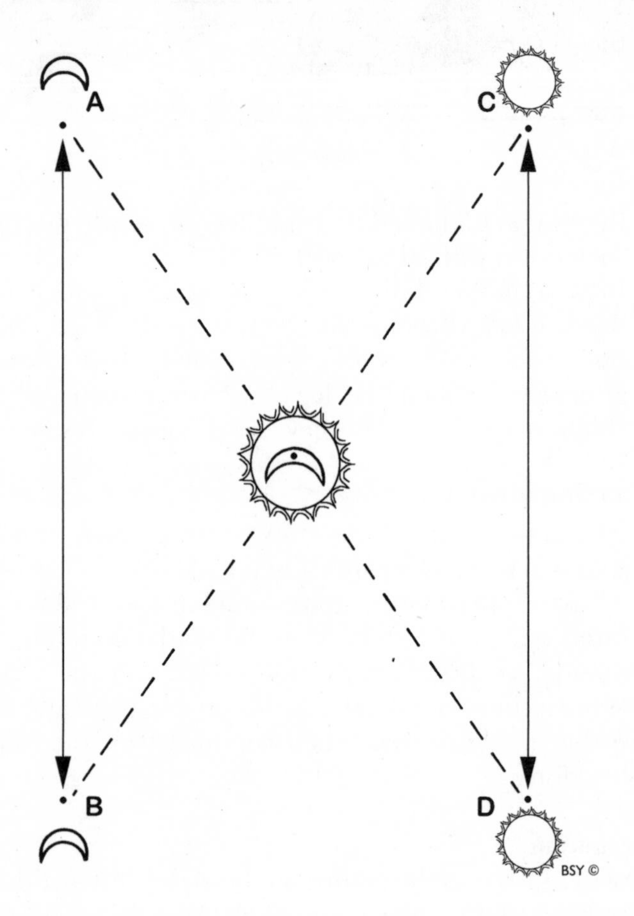

Sun and moon gazing

This practice develops concentration, memory and balancing the breath, while creating a balance between ida and pingala, the moon and sun, thinking and vitality. The technique combines nadi shodhana with a picture and, at the same time, trataka on the centre.

Technique

Look at the sun and moon drawing.

Look at the sun and moon in the middle of the card and see if you can see the lines on the right and left sides.

Keep the eyes fixed on the sun and moon in the centre of the card.

Inhale up the left side and exhale through the dotted line down to the sun at the bottom right. (That is B to A; then A to D.)

Inhale up the sun side and exhale on the moon side, down to the bottom. (D to C; then C to B.)

Again inhale up the moon side, exhale down to the sun. (B to A; A to D.)

Then inhale up the sun side and exhale down to the moon. (D to C; C to B.)

Now, after exhaling on the left side stop the exercise. Rub the hands together above the head until very warm. Put the palms on the eyes and gently move the head from left to right. Sing a song to yourself that you liked as a baby. Then relax the hands and open the eyes.

Practise for five minutes only.

Relaxation and creative visualization practices

There are two techniques given here. The yoga nidra practice must be adapted for children. It must be very quick because children go deeper than adults and it is very difficult to call them back if they are too deeply into the practice. So it should be very short and they should be asked not to sleep.

Technique 1: Yoga nidra

Stage 1: Preparation

Remove your glasses.

Lie down on the floor in shavasana, if possible.

Or sit comfortably at your desk with your hands in your lap and shoulders relaxed.

Relax completely and close your eyes.

Make yourself as comfortable as possible.

Stage 2: Awareness of sounds

First feel your body on the floor.
You are here in this room.
It is (day of the week).
Hear the sounds outside.
Imagine a big circle.
On the circle place the sounds that you hear.
Place the sound (for example, of a car) on the circle.
It is as if the car is moving around that circle.
Inside this circle there is another.
It has the same centre as the first circle.
Hear another sound and then place it on this second circle.
Then another circle inside this one with another sound on it.
I will make three sounds.
First sound: (hands rubbing together).
Second sound: (stepping with feet).
Third sound: (clicking with tongue).
Please remember the sounds.
(The sounds are repeated again).
Now remember the sounds.
Make them come alive on the circles.
Now another sound at the centre of the circle.
Your breath. This is at the centre.

Stage 3: Awareness of touch

Now feel your body on the floor.
Imagine a butterfly settling on the different parts of the body.
Imagine a slight touch of the butterfly on your right hand.
On the top of your head.
Now your neck,
On your right shoulder,
On your left shoulder,
Tip of your nose,
Top of your head.

Stage 4: Visualization

Now the butterfly flies to a tree in bloom.
Oh, there is a bloom from the tree falling down.
No, it is not a bloom but the butterfly, flying again.
You are under that tree and looking at the blue sky through the leaves.
You are breathing energy through the leaves.
You feel happy.
What do you see?
A rocket. A rocket is coming down.
A rocket is landing near you.
Oh, that is fantastic.
Who do you see in that rocket? E.T.! E.T. is coming out.
You know him already. Fantastic, he is coming to you and you are not afraid.
E.T. is asking if you would like to come to his planet. You say, "No, I can't."
He says, "Well, just come and have a look at your house from above." So you agree.
Get into the rocket with E.T.; you are very pleased.
The rocket goes up and you see your house.
You see your mother.
You see your family from above.
And now it is time to come down.
The rocket is coming down and E.T. is saying goodbye.
You are so happy to be alive.
You are so happy to be alive and so relaxed.

Stage 5: Ending the practice

Slowly move your fingers, hands and whole body.
Slowly sit up.
Slowly sit up and open your eyes.
Now sing OM together.
Om, Om, Om.

Hari Om Tat Sat.

Technique 2: Imbibing your favourite colour

Stage 1: Preparation

Lie down on your back.
For the moment you feel the contact of the floor.
Feel as if you are sending roots into the ground.
You are grounded.

Stage 2: Visualization

Imagine you are a little island in the sea.
A little island with palm trees, under the blue sky.
And your body is that island with its curves, its gulfs and creeks. The forest is your hair and your two eyes are two beautiful lakes.
In between your fingers are nice little harbours.
Imagine that you hear the sound of waves along the beach; and the waves are your breath.
Count 7 waves or breaths that you are listening to...
When you finish, imagine that you are floating above your island and you see it from above.
You are smiling, with the breeze in your hair.

Stage 3: Awareness of colours

You are floating and come to a rainbow.
You are going to bathe in the colours of the rainbow.
Please note which colour you prefer to bathe in.
Red, imagine you are all red and floating in red.
Orange, yellow, green, blue, dark blue, purple, gold, golden colour...pause.
Now I will repeat them and you pick the colour you prefer. Golden colour, purple, dark blue, blue, green, yellow, orange, red...pause.

Stage 4: Breath awareness

Now imagine you are still bathing in your favourite colour, while on the floor.
You are breathing it in.
While breathing it out, it permeates your whole body.
While you inhale, it comes from outside.
While you exhale it spreads into your arms, legs and into your trunk. It is spreading into your head and neck.

Now feel that the quality of your favourite colour is in you. It has given you its quality.
And when you get up you will retain it.
You will feel as beautiful and as fresh as your favourite colour. Maybe tomorrow it will be another colour, but today bathe in today's favourite colour.

Stage 5: Feelings

Slowly stop that image.
Feel how well you are.
Remember a time when you were so happy because you had learned something pleasant,
something difficult which you had finally mastered.
How happy you felt that you could do it at last.
And how your parents congratulated you for doing it.
This feeling you are going to keep with you.

Stage 6: Ending the practice

Slowly move the fingers. Slowly move the whole body, then open the eyes and sit up.

Hari Om Tat Sat.

Using the techniques with children

The teacher should never constrain the motivation and initiative of the child by failing to make the sessions interesting and varied. The practices should always be presented in a spirit of creative imagination and variation. Many of the same exercises can be presented in different ways.

Bodily and mental dissipation of energy is the most important problem for the school child; a lack of a centring within themselves. A mandala is a universal symbol made up of patterns, colours, sounds, etc. Concentration on these geometrical designs helps the child to centre himself and also aids in mathematics, geometry and trigonometry studies. The importance of the child actually physically performing a geometrical design, for example rotating 60 degrees around himself in a circle, then 180 degrees so that he is facing in the opposite direction, etc., is finally being understood and implemented with great success by educators involved in teaching these higher mathematics to mentally disabled children with the aid of computers.

It should never be forgotten that the child is a harmonized being. Therefore, he is more delicate than an adult in many ways. It is essential to be particularly careful in these cases:

- Before starting to do any flexion of the spinal column the child must learn to maintain correct posture, while both sitting and standing.
- It is important that before the child does backward bending postures, the pelvis is tilted slightly.

Anyone involved in education knows that we should work progressively from the most simple to the most complex techniques. Broadly speaking there are two principal phases:

1. A preparation phase of awareness of the different body parts, natural breath, and of mental agility and release of tension. It must be obvious that one cannot bring influence to bear on something one does not know about.
2. A more active phase of work on the self and a phase of increasing depth.

All the aspects of the child's personality should be simultaneously brought into harmony. It would, therefore, be wrong to work exclusively on the body or the mind. The activities should be synthesized. We present a great variety of exercises, both physical and mental, in the knowledge that the human being forms a whole, which is one, and that there is always an interaction between the physical body, the emotions and the mind.

17

Introduction to Asana

When you are starting to teach yoga to children, it is important that at least a basic knowledge of anatomy and physiology is at hand. It is important that the teacher bears in mind always that his body and those of his students are at two different stages of development and therefore he needs to understand how physical and cognitive growth takes place in the child.

Body growth in children is a continuing process throughout the years of childhood and adolescence. It is exceedingly rapid in the first two years of life and less so during the middle years of childhood. Later there is a growth spurt in relation to puberty followed by cessation of growth when the adult height is reached. Growth and development in the skeleton, or bone age, have been described by Tanner and his colleagues using X-rays of the left wrist and hand as a method of assessment. Functional and structural changes which the body undergoes at puberty makes it capable of procreation. In both boys and girls the subcutaneous fat on the trunk and limbs increases in thickness rapidly during the first years of life and then decreases during the middle years of childhood.

The brain has a rapid increase in size during the first few years of life. In developing the visual systems, Bower, among others, has shown that the primary visual system localized in the superior colliculi of the corpora quadrigemina complex, the 'where' vision, is highly operative in the neonate. The secondary, 'what' vision associated with the visual cortex of the brain develops very rapidly in cats at an early age as shown by Hubel and Wiezel. They demonstrated the importance of the growth taking place within the visual system at an early age, and the effect of the environment on its ultimate perceptual abilities.

So the physical bodies of the students whom we are teaching are still changing and yoga asana and pranayama can have a very direct effect upon their anatomy and physiology.

Disorders of growth may be caused by many factors. Organic disorders of the central nervous system and the cardiovascular, respiratory, renal, haematopoietic or alimentary systems may interfere with growth. In addition, adverse psychological factors due to an unhappy home life are very important in this respect. Children whose growth has been slowed by illness show a greater than normal rate of growth upon correction of the disorder. This rapid phase growth is called 'catch up' growth.

Yoga asanas are classified according to either difficulty of performance or dynamic/static practices. When teaching children, the easy asanas should be taught first, then the intermediate, progressing on to the more difficult and advanced postures. For children's classes the asanas taught are predominantly dynamic practices but some static asanas should also be taught, because the children should also be able to sit quietly without movement for short periods. As the child grows older and matures, he himself will begin to enjoy and demand more static postures.

Dynamic or static practices

Dynamic practices involve dynamic movements of the body. In this book we will refer to them as asanas, although the precise meaning of the word asana is 'steady pose'. This group of dynamic practices are not intended to develop muscles, but to loosen up the body and remove stagnant blood in different parts of the body. They help tighten the skin and muscles, strengthen the lungs and encourage movement in the digestive and excretory systems. They are particularly useful for children. Dynamic practices include surya namaskara, chandra namaskara, warrior sequence, pawanmuktasana series, dynamic paschimottanasana and dynamic bhujangasana.

Static practices are performed with little or no movement of the body, often remaining in one position for a few minutes or more. These are intended to gently massage the internal organs, glands and muscles as well as to relax the nerves throughout the body. They are specifically concerned with bringing tranquility to the mind and preparing the practitioner for the higher practices of yoga such as pranayama, relaxation or concentration. Some prepare the body for meditation by making the body steady and firm. In these practices the respiration rate is generally slowed down and the practitioner directs his or her awareness to one particular part of the body, depending upon the asana.

General advice and precautions

Before beginning the practice of asanas, certain precautions must be taken:

Breathing: Always breathe through the nose unless instructed otherwise. In dynamic asanas the breath and movements are slow, long and coordinated. Follow the individual instructions given for the static asanas.

Body awareness: The difference between dynamic yogasanas and gymnastics is the speed at which the movements are executed and body awareness. Asana practice without awareness of the body is not yoga. Body awareness induces relaxation while in the posture. When the asana is maintained with tension, it will have the opposite effect. For example, if sarvangasana, the shoulderstand, is practised with the body tense, the sex glands can be overstimulated resulting in a continual emission of semen, rather than a reduction in production of the spermatozoa.

Relaxation: Practise shavasana before the asana session so that you begin with the body relaxed and mind and emotions centred on the practices at hand. If during asana practice you feel tired, then do shavasana. After completing the asanas, lie down in shavasana for at least 10 to 15 minutes to remove any fatigue.

Sequence: Asanas should be practised first, then pranayama, ending with relaxation or concentration.

Time of practice: Asanas can be practised at any time of the day, except after meals. However, the best time to do all yoga practices is in the early morning. The atmosphere is pure, quiet and filled with solar radiation. The activities of the stomach and intestines have stopped. The mind has no deep impressions on the conscious level and it is empty of thoughts in preparation for the day ahead.

Place of practice: The place of practice should be a clean, well-ventilated room which is quiet and insect free. If possible practise outdoors in a garden or pleasant surrounding but only if the air is free of pollution and there is no strong wind or cold air. If introducing yoga into the classroom, make sure that there is enough space to carry out the practices, free from furniture if possible. Most accidents occur when you fall against an object rather than falling from an asana. When the classroom has fixed furniture then the asanas have to be adapted to suit the situation. Some practices can be done while sitting at a desk.

Blanket: Practise on a folded blanket or a small carpet, laid on a level floor. Do not use foam rubber or air mattresses.

Clothing: During the practice of asanas it is better to wear loose, comfortable and light clothing. Remove spectacles, watches and any body ornaments.

Empty bowels and bladder: The bowels should be evacuated and the bladder empty before asana practice.

Empty stomach: Asanas should be done only when the stomach is empty, therefore, early morning practice before eating is best. At least three or four hours should elapse after a heavy meal before starting the asana practice.

Diet: There are no special dietary rules for practitioners of asanas, though it is better to eat natural foods and in reasonable moderation. Contrary to popular opinion, yoga does not say you must become a vegetarian, though in the more advanced stages it does advise people to do so.

If one is suffering from a particular disease then dietary restrictions should be imposed in accordance with the ailment, and advice should be sought from an expert.

No straining: Never exert undue force or strain while doing or trying to do an asana. Regular practice will remove stiff joints and muscles and make even the most advanced asanas easy.

Limitations: All age groups, both male and female, can practise the asanas included in this book. Many asanas can be practised in some form even by severely disabled children.

Restrictions: Anyone suffering from any form of chronic disease such as ulcers, tuberculosis, hernia, slipped disc, should consult a doctor and an experienced yoga therapist before commencing asanas. Sufferers of dizziness or high blood pressure should not attempt inverted postures, dynamic spinal twists or head rolls. Anyone with pus in the ears, detached retina, myopia, etc. should not do inverted postures where there is pressure on the head from the floor.

Closing of eyes: Dynamic asanas and those involving balance are best practised with eyes open. As one advances the eyes can be closed.

Daily practice: It is not necessary to practise all 30 or 84 known classic asanas. There should always be a balance in the chosen asana, ensuring that glandular stimulation received from the posture is well balanced. When determining the asanas for a class or for one's own daily practice, there are six main elements to be included in the choice of asana.

1. A forward bending asana to keep the spine supple in the forward direction.
2. A backward bending asana, arching, as a counterbalance.
3. Twisting asana for maintaining supple lateral movements of the spine.

4. Balancing asana. This is a very important element that should not be left out. Balance is an ability we acquire as children and lose as we become older. Many doctors, especially those working with geriatrics, suggest that balancing exercises should be practised daily in order to maintain this very important ability that we learned as children.
5. An inverted asana for stimulation of glands in the head and reversing the pressure of blood flowing to the lower extremities.
6. A sitting asana for developing the ability to sit for some time without moving the body in order to practise pranayama and meditation.

18

Pawanmuktasana Series

Pawanmuktasana is a group of exercises which release wind and gases from the body. *Pawan* means 'wind'; *mukta* means 'release', *asana* means 'posture'. The pawanmuktasana series is very simple, yet it is most effective in regulating what are referred to in India as the humours: phlegm or *kapha*, wind or *vata* and acid/bile, *pitta*.

According to the ancient medical science known as ayurveda, these three humours control all the functions of the body. If any irregularity arises in their functions, negative reactions take place in the metabolism of the body and disease results.

Physical yoga

Pawanmuktasana are simple exercises for the development of body awareness. During the practice of each exercise the children should be encouraged to feel the part of the body being used. Since one covers all the body parts with these exercises it is like giving oneself a complete external physical examination. One quickly notices the difference in development of the two body sides. If pawanmuktasana is introduced to children it will facilitate equal development of the body, and both right and left hemispheres of the brain.

The pawanmuktasana series should be practised very slowly. Since slow motion movements need more attention, this helps to develop concentration and in itself helps to induce relaxation. It is important to build in the discipline of counting from the very beginning.

Pawanmuktasana movements are simple; all yoga exercises and asanas are slow, conscious stretching or conscious postures and not the fast energy burning movements that we experience in gymnastics or keep fit classes. Problems such as straining or pulled ligaments or muscles should never occur since one should at all times be completely aware of the movement in the particular body part being used. This awareness is the important difference between yoga asanas and gymnastics.

The pawanmuktasana series of exercises is divided into three distinct groups: anti-rheumatic, anti-gastric, and energy-releasing.

Pawanmuktasana 1

ANTI-RHEUMATIC ASANAS

These exercises will beneficially influence the different joints and organs of the body. Though they seem simple, they have subtle effects on the practitioner. This group of exercises is also known as *sukshma vyayam* in Sanskrit, meaning 'subtle exercises'. This series of exercises should be performed at the beginning of the daily asana session to loosen the joints and make the muscles supple.

Pawanmuktasana like any other yoga asana should be presented and adapted to the age of the children. They may also be applied in a classroom situation in many ways. Good examples presented by RYE to balance the physical development of children can be found in chapter 15. In a playgroup environment or with pre-school children it is fun to play with finger paints or with two brushes while rotating wrists or using individual fingers for painting. There are many songs and games used in playgroups that are ideal ways of developing awareness of the different body parts.

Our first set of pawanmuktasana exercises, the anti-rheumatic, is a systematic movement of all the joints in the body. The child is asked to think and feel more in terms of the bony structure than the muscular structure. With small children, let them look at pictures of a skeleton, pointing out the different joints.

Parambhik Sthiti (base position)

Sit with the legs stretched in front of the body.
Place the hands on the floor slightly behind the trunk.
There is a slight backward inclination of the body.
The legs are slightly apart.

Practice 1: Padanguli Naman (toe bending)

Sit in the base position.
Become aware of the toes.
Slowly bend the toes of both feet forward and backward without moving the ankles.
Repeat 10 times slowly.

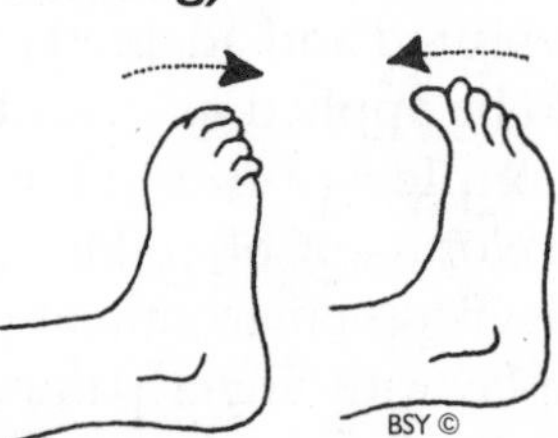

Practice 2: Toe spreading

Sit in the base position.
Bring the awareness to the toes – spread them as far apart as possible. Relax, allow the toes to come together again.
Repeat slowly and smoothly 10 times.

Practice note: Avoid causing cramp by tensing too strongly. If the child is unable to spread the toes, the hands can be used to spread the toes, one foot at a time.

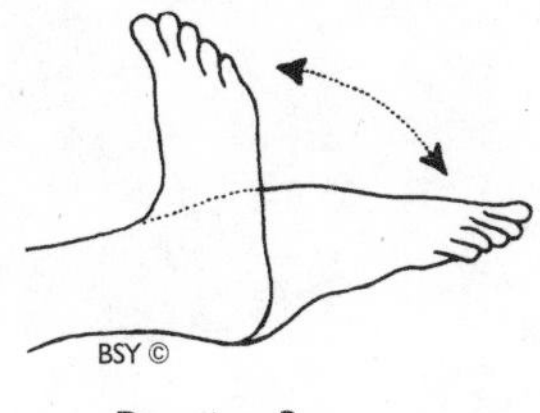

Practice 3

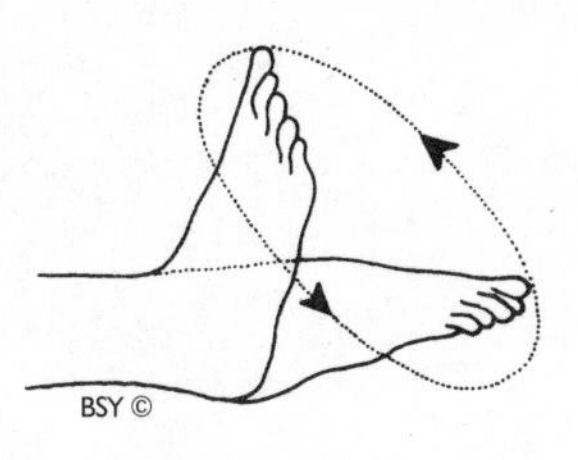

Practice 4

Practice 3: Goolf Naman (ankle bending)

Sit in the base position.
Bring the awareness to the ankles.
Slowly bend the feet as far forward as possible.
Then slowly bend them as far back as possible.
Repeat 10 times with awareness, at a slow, even rhythm.

Practice 4: Goolf Chakra (ankle rotation)

Sit in the base position with the feet slightly separated.
Become aware of the ankles.
Slowly rotate the right foot 10 times in a clockwise direction. Try to make the movement as wide as possible. Imagine that you have a piece of chalk on the end of the big toe and you are drawing a large circle with the chalk.
Now rotate the right foot 10 times anti-clockwise.
Repeat the practice with the left foot.
Now repeat with both feet, moving them together in the same direction.
The legs and body should remain relaxed with the only movement being in the ankles.

Practice 5: Goolf Ghoornan (ankle crank)

Sit in the base position.
Bend the right knee and place the right ankle on the left thigh. The right hand rests on the right knee or ankle, the left hand holds the toes of the right foot.
Bring the awareness to the right ankle. Rotate the right foot with the left hand 10 times clockwise and then 10 times anti-clockwise.
Return to the base position. Repeat with the left foot.

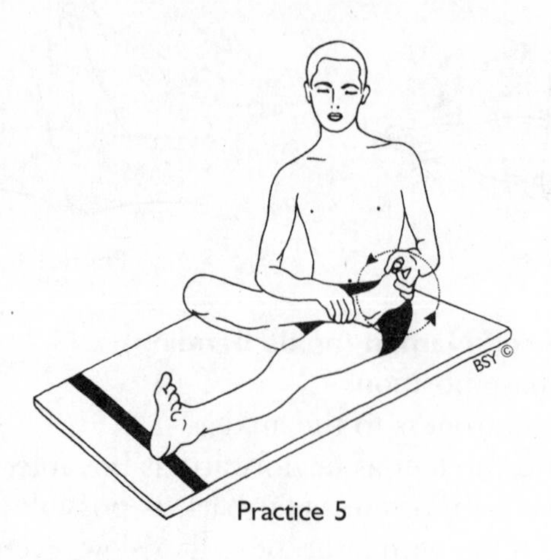

Practice 5

Practice 6: Janu Naman (knee bending)

Sit in the base position.

Bring the awareness to the hip and the knee. Bend the right knee and hold the back of the thigh with clasped hands. Bend the right leg at the knee so that the thigh is close to the chest and the right heel close to the buttocks.

Straighten the arms and leg but do not allow the leg or foot to touch the ground.

Repeat 10 times, then return to the base position.

Repeat with the left leg.

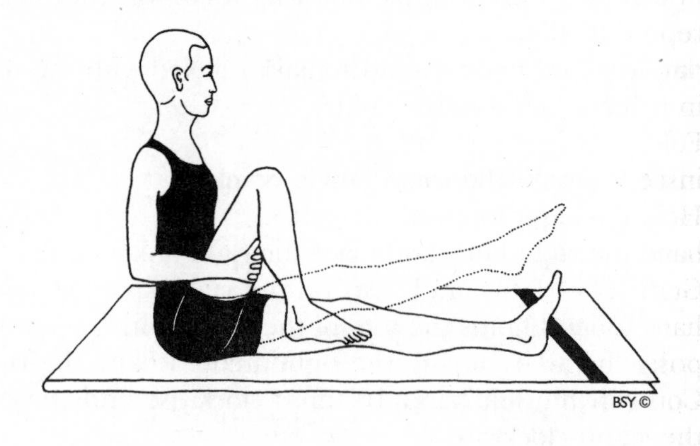

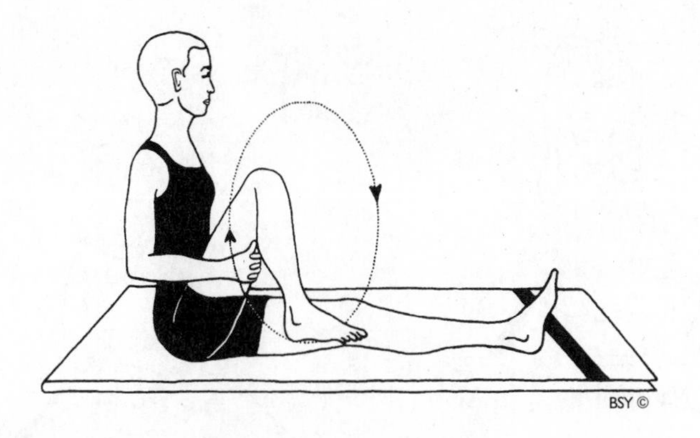

Practice 7: Janu Chakra (knee crank)

Sit in the base position.

Bend the right leg at the knee.

Clasp the hands around the back of the thigh, bringing the thigh close to the trunk.

Become aware of the knee. Rotate the lower leg in a circular motion around the knee 10 times clockwise and 10 times anti-clockwise.

Return to the base position and repeat with the left leg.

Practice 8: Ardha Titali Asana (half butterfly)

This asana has six variations.

Practise one after the other with the right leg. Then repeat the sequence with the left leg.

Variation 1: Sit in the base position, with the legs outstretched in front of the body.

Fold the right leg and place the right sole against the inside of the left thigh.

Hold the right foot with the left hand and place the right hand on the top of the bent right knee.

Gently move the bent leg up and down with the right hand, allowing the muscles of the leg to relax as much as possible.

Continue this practice until after some weeks or months the right knee starts to touch, or nearly touch, the floor.

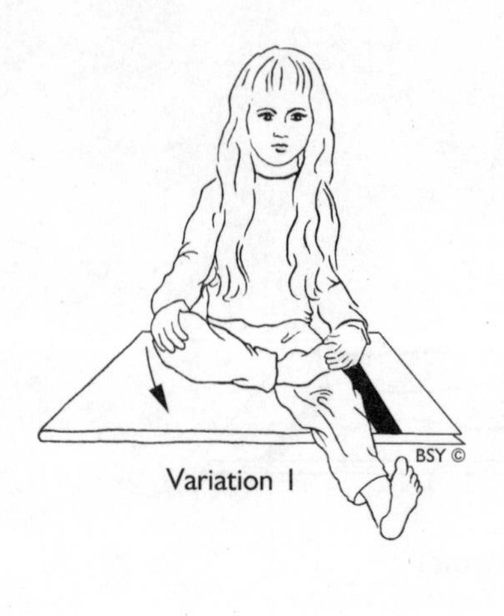

Variation 1

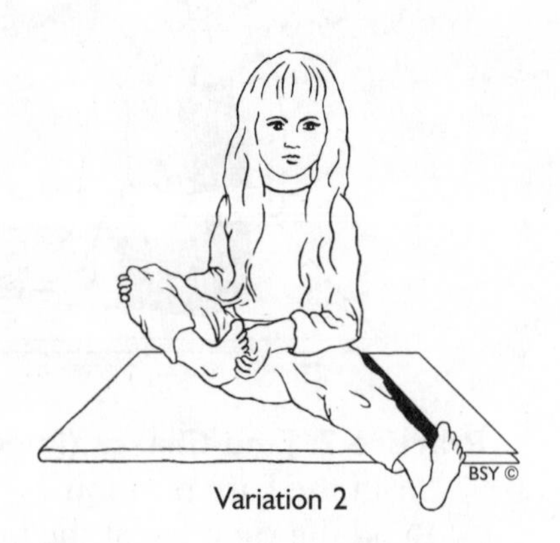

Variation 2

Variation 2: Sitting in half butterfly, hold the right knee with the right hand and the right foot with the left hand.
Push gently with the left hand moving the knee to the right towards the side. Keep the foot and knee as close to the floor as possible.
Then relax and let the right foot come back to rest on the left thigh.
Repeat about 10 times.

Variation 3

Variation 3: Sitting in half butterfly, hold the toes of the right foot with the right hand and the heel with the left hand.
Raise the foot up to about face level. Do not straighten the knee or ankle but keep them slightly bent.
Gently lower the foot back to rest on the left thigh.
Repeat about 10 times.

Variation 4

Variation 4: Sitting in half butterfly, hold the right foot as before. Raise the foot up to eye level.
Bend the elbows and pull the foot gently towards the face so the toes come to touch the eyebrow centre. The foot is brought to the head, not the head down to the foot.
Straighten the arms and repeat 10 times.

Variation 5

Variation 5: Sit in half butterfly, with the right foot resting in the hands, the right knee pointing towards the ceiling.
Make sure that the right arm is inside the right leg.
Push the foot up, so the the right knee moves past the shoulder and to the back.
Relax and let the foot rest in the hands on the floor.
Repeat about 10 times.

Variation 6

Variation 6: Sitting in half butterfly, hold the lower right leg at the calf with both hands, making sure that the right arm is under the right leg.
Slide the right arm further and further under the right lower leg, pushing the leg up and back.
Straighten the back so that the inside thigh is resting against the back and the lower right leg is sticking over the shoulder.
Let the leg rest on the shoulder for a few seconds.
Lower the leg slowly back to the floor into the half butterfly.
Now repeat the six variations with the left leg.

Benefits: This series of movements is very important for maintaining suppleness in the joints of the legs and thighs. When stiffness has already occurred, this series is most beneficial in making all the joints flexible. After some days or weeks of practice, the knees should rest comfortably on the floor without effort.

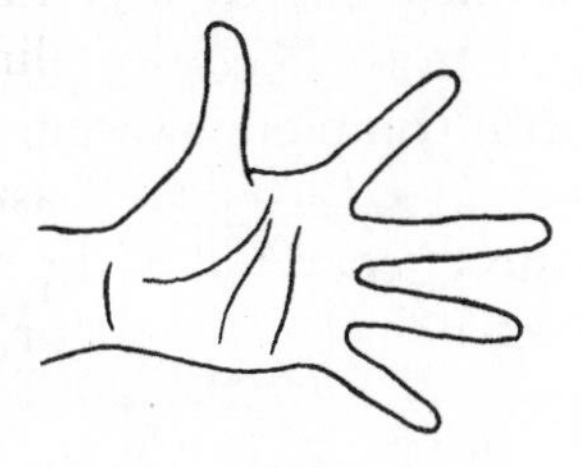

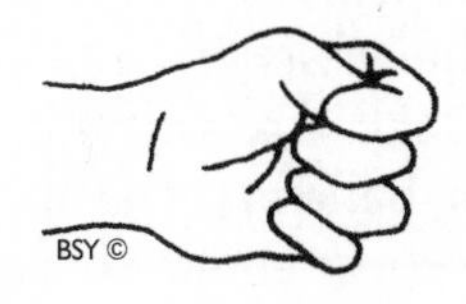

Mushtika Bandhana (hand clenching)

Sit in the base position, or in sukhasana.

Raise the arms and stretch them in front of the body at shoulder level.

The awareness is in the hands and fingers.

Open the hands and spread the fingers as wide as possible, creating as much tension as is comfortable, then relax the hands.

Now, folding the thumbs inside, clench the fists as tightly as is comfortable, then relax. It is important that the thumbs are placed inside the fists in order to achieve maximum movement in the thumb joints.

This is one round.

Practise flowing from tension to relaxation to tension etc.

After 10 rounds, relax the arms and bring the hands to the knees.

Manibandha Naman (wrist bending)

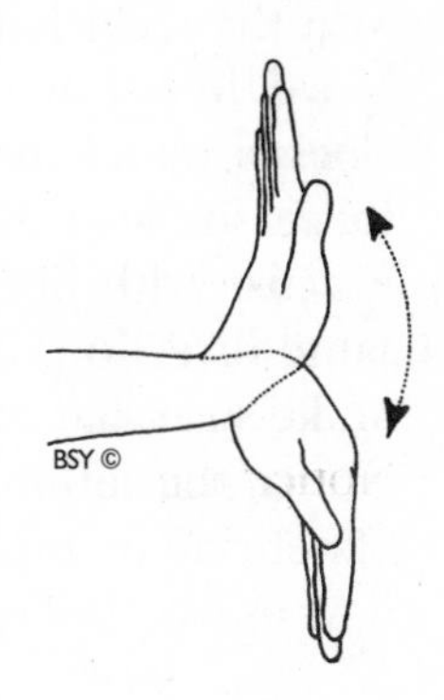

Sit in the base position, or adopt sukhasana.

Stretch the arms in front of the body at shoulder level, with palms facing away from the body and fingertips pointing towards the ceiling. Bring the awareness to the wrists.

Bend the hands forward from the wrists so that the fingers point to the floor.

Slowly return them to point towards the ceiling. This is one round.

Repeat 10 times, slowly and with complete awareness of the wrists.

Make sure that there is no tension generated in the arms or hands.

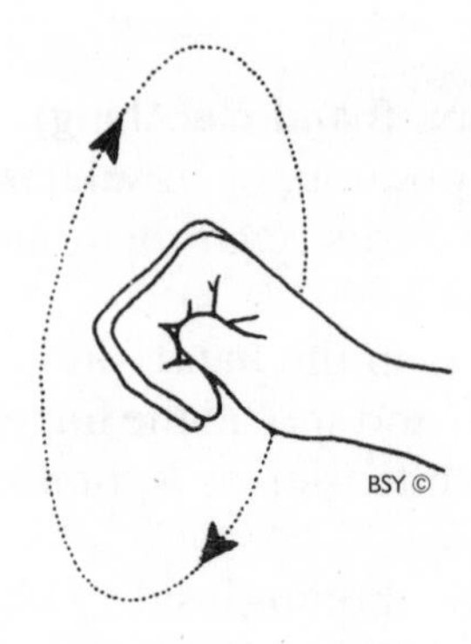

Manibandha Chakra (wrist joint rotation)

Sit in the base position or sukhasana.

Extend the right arm in front of the body at shoulder level.

The left hand may be used to support the right arm at the elbow.

Bring the awareness to the wrist and hand. Make a fist with the right hand.

Move the fist in a complete circle, slowly rotating 10 times clockwise and then 10 times anti-clockwise.

Relax the arm. Repeat with the left hand.

Practise with both hands together, moving them in the same direction.

Make sure that only the wrist is moving and not the arm.

Notice the difference between the two hands.

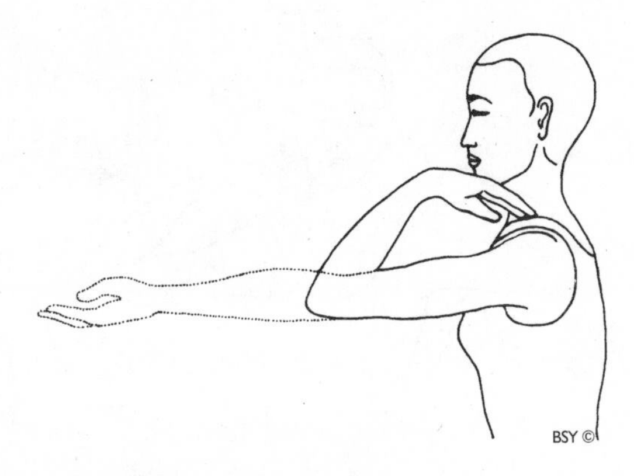

Kehuni Naman (elbow bending)

Sit in the base position or sukhasana.

Raise the arms and stretch them out in front with the palms upward.

The awareness should be at the elbows with no tension in the arms or hands.

Slowly bend the elbows and bring the tips of the fingers to touch the shoulders, keeping the elbows at chest level.

Then slowly straighten the arms again.

Repeat 10 times, then rest the hands on the knees.

Raise both arms again, this time to the sides, palms upward.

Retaining the awareness at the elbows, slowly bend the elbows and touch the shoulders with the fingertips.

Slowly straighten the arms to the sides.

Repeat 10 times.

Keep the back, neck and shoulders relaxed throughout this practice.

Skandha Chakra (shoulder socket rotation)

Sit in the base position or sukhasana.

Place the fingertips of the right hand on the right shoulder and slowly draw a large circle with the right elbow.

Practise slowly 10 times clockwise and 10 times anti-clockwise.

Repeat on the left side.

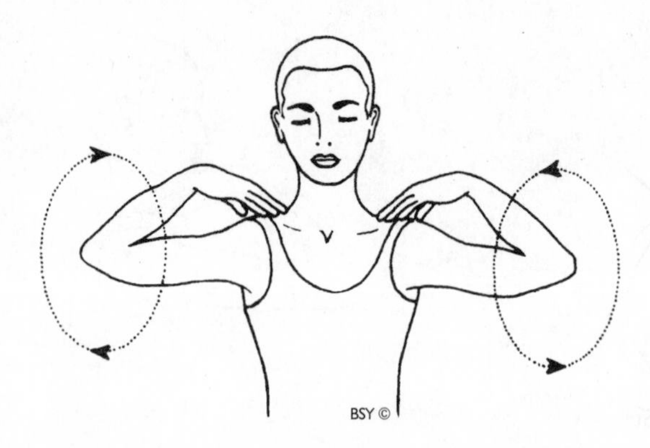

Then rotate both elbows together in a large circle, trying to touch the chest, ears and sides of the trunk.

Benefits: Remember this is a ball and socket joint so achieve as much movement as is comfortable. Awareness is in the shoulder joints and the muscles of the back. This practice is especially good for children who have been sitting, writing or drawing for some hours each day.

Greeva Sanchalana (neck movements)

Stage 1: Forward and back

Sit in the base position or sukhasana.

Bring the awareness to the neck.

Slowly exhale and tilt the head forward, bringing the chin close to the chest.

Inhale and slowly move the head back as far as is comfortable. Do not strain.

Repeat slowly 10 times with the eyes closed.

Stage 2: Side to side

Sit in the base position, with the eyes closed.

Turn the head to face the right so that the chin is in line with the shoulder.

Slowly turn the head back to the centre and around to the left so that the chin is in line with the left shoulder.

Inhale while turning to the front.

Exhale while turning to the side.

This is one round. Practise 10 rounds.

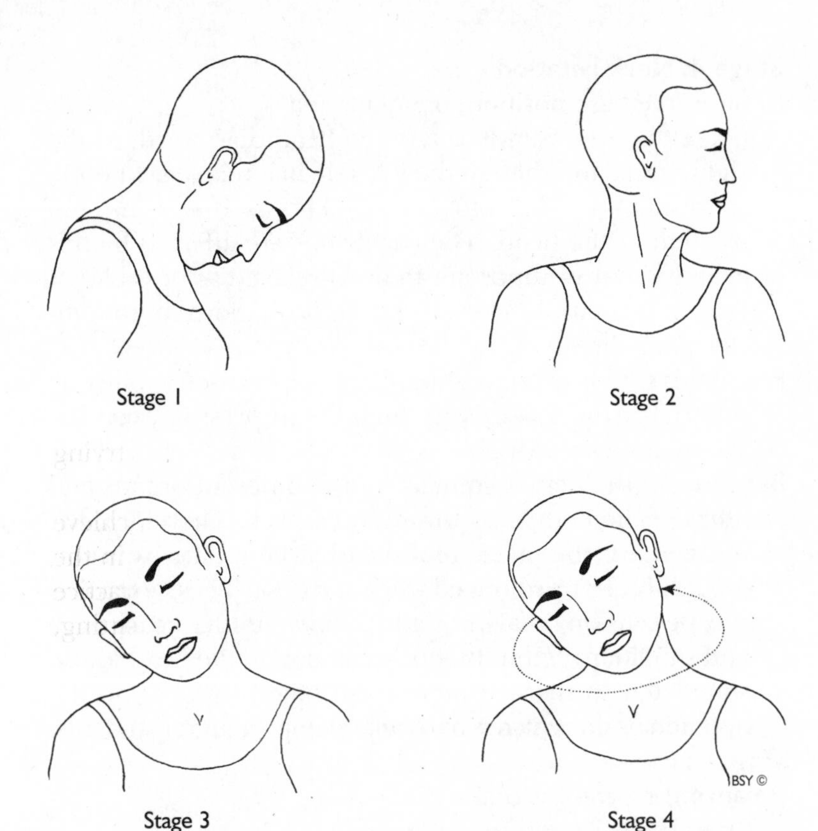

Stage 3: Right to left

Facing forward, place the palms on the knees and straighten the elbows. This will cause the shoulders to be slightly raised.

Close the eyes. Slowly tilt the head to the right and try to touch the right ear to the right shoulder.

Then move the head to the left and try to touch the left ear to the left shoulder.

Inhale as the head moves up.

Exhale as the head moves to the side.

Practise 10 times to each side.

Do not force the ear to touch the shoulder; it is the movement of the neck which is important.

Stage 4: Neck rotation

Sit in the base position, or sukhasana.

Close the eyes. Slowly rotate the head downward, to the right, back, and then to the left side in a relaxed, smooth, rhythmic, circular movement. This is one complete rotation of the head. The ear drums are affected by this exercise so it is important to be as relaxed as possible.

Repeat 5 rotations clockwise then 5 rotations in an anti-clockwise direction.

Precautions: This exercise should not be practised by anyone suffering from low or very high blood pressure, cervical spondylosis, or vertigo.

Benefits: All the nerves connecting the different organs and limbs of the body pass through the neck. Therefore, the muscles of the neck and head accumulate tension, especially after prolonged work at a desk. These exercises release tension, heaviness and stiffness in the head, neck and shoulder region. Blood circulation to the head is also stimulated so there is more fresh blood supplied to the eyes and brain, which is particularly important for students.

Balancing on the buttocks

Sit in the base position.

Bend the knees, bringing the thighs close to the trunk, and clasp the hands under the thighs.

Slowly raise the feet from the floor, easing back onto the buttocks to balance. Keep the eyes open and stare at a fixed point in front to maintain balance.

After practising for a while, close the eyes and relax the body as much as possible, still maintaining the posture.

Begin practising for 1 minute, then gradually increase to 3 to 5 minutes.

With eyes open, maintaining the balance, rotate the lower legs slowly 10 times clockwise then 10 times anti-clockwise.

Return to the base position.

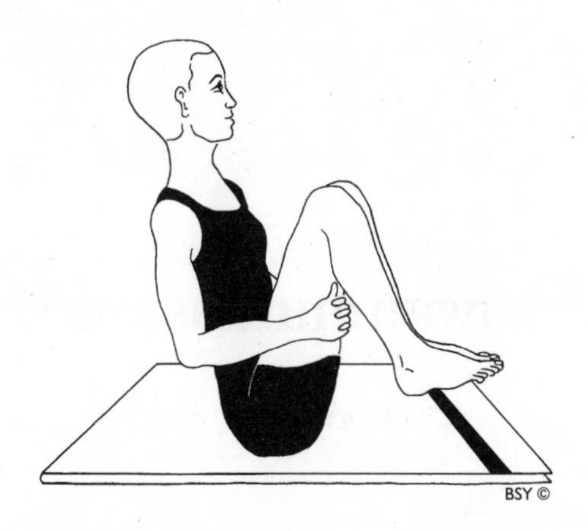

Sukhasana (easy pose)

Sit with the legs stretched in front of the body.
Bend the right leg and place the foot under the left thigh.
Bend the left leg and place the foot under the right thigh.
Place the hands on the knees, and keep the spine, neck and head in a straight line.
If this posture is difficult at first, a cloth or belt may be tied around the knees and lower back for support.

Pawanmuktasana 2

ANTI-GASTRIC ASANAS

In this group of exercises the children are asked to synchronize the physical movements of the body with deep relaxed breathing. Breath and body movements should be of equal length. The student should be reminded to observe the breath and heartbeat before and between exercises. If either are fast, just wait until they are normal before starting the next posture. The most relaxing pose is shavasana, but it can be done while sitting or standing.

Spinal massage

Stage 1: Lie flat on the back, legs folded up to the chest.
Wrap the arms around the knees and pull them gently towards the chest as you exhale.
While inhaling, relax the pull on the knees but do not place the feet back onto the floor. This results in a rocking movement.

Repeat at least 10 times and then stretch the legs out, assuming shavasana.

Stage 2: Lie flat on the back as in the previous exercise with the legs folded up to the chest, holding the knees with the hands.

Rotate the knees as if you are drawing circles with them, 10 times clockwise and 10 times anti-clockwise.

Exhale as the knees are brought close to the body and inhale as they are moved away from the body.

When completed, exhale while stretching the legs out and assuming shavasana.

This exercise benefits the lumbar nerves and muscles.

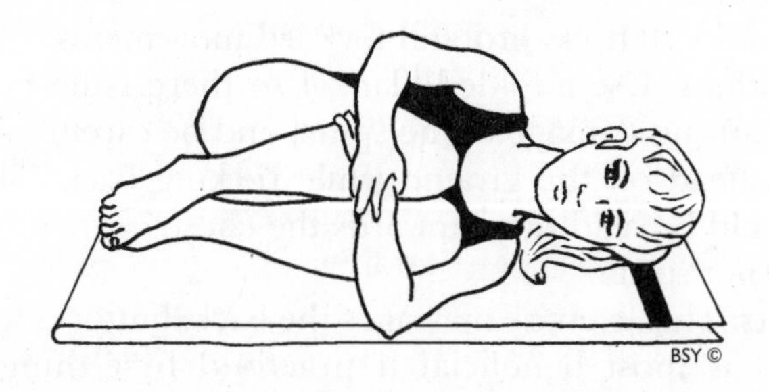

Jhulana Lurhakanasana (rocking and rolling)

Stage 1: Lie on the back, the legs folded up to the chest.

Interlock the fingers and clasp the legs around the knees.

Roll the body from side to side, touching the elbow and the side of the legs to the floor.

Rolling to the right and then to the left is one round.

Do 10 rounds, rolling very slowly and carefully with complete awareness placed on the entire spinal column.

When completed, exhale while returning legs to the floor.

Stage 2: Sit in the squatting position with the buttocks just above the floor.

Interlock the fingers of both hands and wrap them around both knees. Rock the whole body forwards and backwards on the spine.

Try to come into a squatting pose on the feet when rocking forward.

Do 5 to 10 backward and forward movements.

Precautions: Use a folded blanket so there is no possibility of causing damage to the spine, and be careful not to hit the head on the ground while rocking back. The head should be held tilted towards the chest.

Do not strain.

Benefits: This exercise massages the back, buttocks and hips, and is most beneficial if practised first thing in the morning. It should not be performed by anyone with spinal problems.

Supta Pawanmuktasana I (simple leg lock pose)

Lie in shavasana. Become aware of the whole body and make sure that it is relaxed and steady.

Slowly bend the right knee and bring the thigh near the chest.

Interlock the fingers and place them over the knee.

Inhale and pull the knee as close to the chest as possible while retaining the breath inside.

Slowly exhale, return the right leg to the floor and resume shavasana.

Check the breath and heartbeat. If they are normal, repeat the same procedure with the left leg.

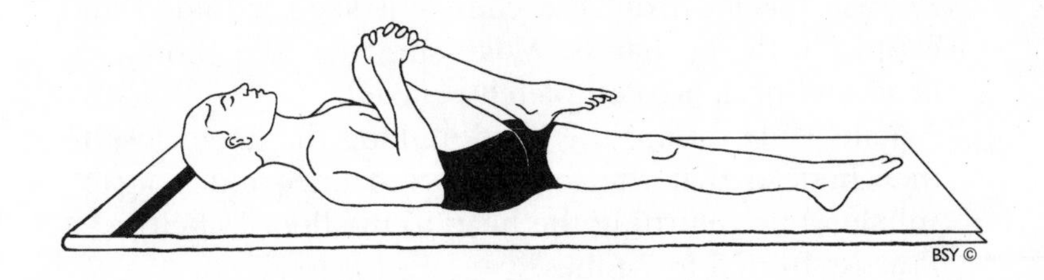

Then repeat with both legs together.

The right leg, left leg and both legs together equals one round.

Practise 5 to 10 rounds.

Benefits: As a general rule, the lungs are empty when one practises bending forward or bringing the knees close to the chest, causing pressure on the lungs. However, in this exercise the lungs are filled. The extended diaphragm gently presses against the abdominal organs, bringing stimulation through activation of pressure receptors, and helping to remove constipation and flatulence.

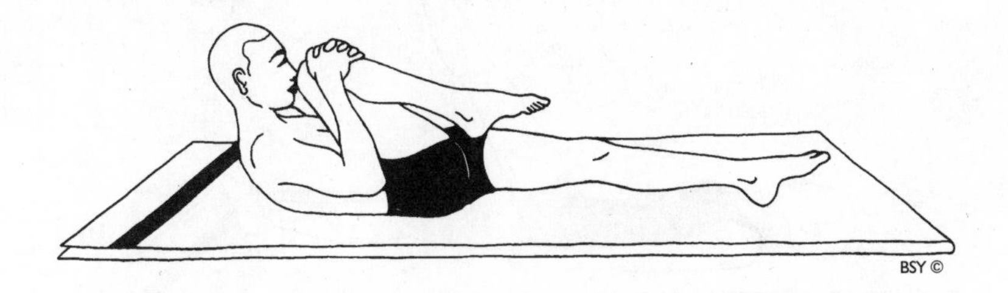

Supta Pawanmuktasana 2 (leg lock pose)

Lie in shavasana.

Inhale slowly, bend the right knee and bring it close to the chest. Interlock the fingers and place them over the knee.

While exhaling, raise the head and pull the knee close to the chest so that the forehead or nose touches the knee.

Hold as long as is comfortable with the breath held out.

Inhale and bring the head back to the floor.

Release the leg from the chest but keep it folded and clasped with the hands. Make sure that the shoulders, head and neck are completely relaxed.

Exhale while raising the head, pulling the knee close to the chest so that the forehead and knee touch again. Inhale while returning the head to the floor as before. Practise from 3 to 7 times.

Then, while exhaling, return the right leg to the floor and resume shavasana.

When the heartbeat and breath rate are normal, repeat the same procedure with the left leg, and then with both legs together.

Benefits: This exercise has a direct massaging influence on the abdomen and digestive organs and is, therefore, highly recommended for anyone suffering from flatulence and constipation. It strengthens and relaxes the lower back muscles and loosens the spinal vertebrae.

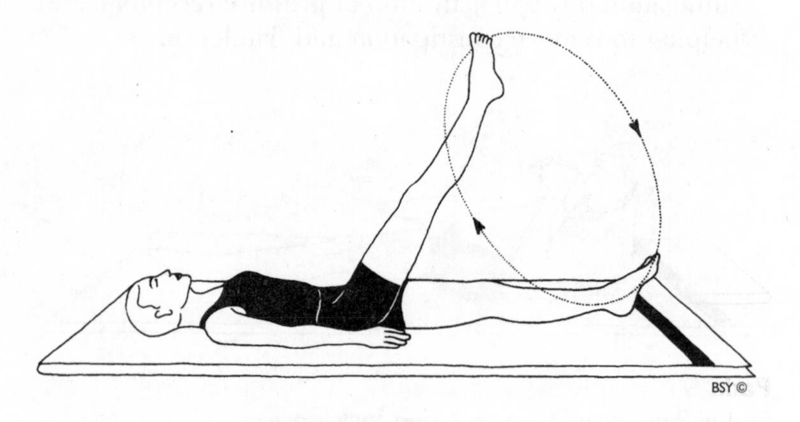

Chakra Padasana (leg rotation)

Lie in shavasana. Become calm and steady.

Raise the right leg 5 cm off the ground, keeping the knee straight.

Rotate the right leg clockwise 10 times, making a large circle. The heel should not touch the floor during the rotation.

Breathe deeply.
Return the leg to the floor.
Rotate 10 times in the opposite direction.
Repeat the same procedure with the left leg.
Then rotate both legs clockwise and then anti-clockwise up to 5 times.
Keep the rest of the body, including the head, flat on the floor.
Always check the breath and heartbeat after completion of the 10 rounds and allow them to become normal before starting again.
Remember that the pelvic joint is a ball and socket so try to get maximum movement during the exercise without any strain.

Benefits: Good for hip joints, obesity, toning of abdominal and spinal muscles.

Pada Sanchalanasana (cycling)

Lying in shavasana, become calm and steady.
Raise the right leg and make cycling movements as if cycling forward at least 10 times, then cycle backwards 10 times.
Repeat the same with the left leg.
Then cycle with both legs, alternating as if riding a bicycle.
Breathe deeply. Keep the rest of the body, including the head, flat on the floor.

After completing each part of the exercise, rest in shavasana until respiration returns to normal.
Do not strain.

Benefits: Good for hip and knee joints. Strengthens abdominal and lower back muscles.

Shashankasana (pose of the moon or hare pose)

Sit in vajrasana and place the hands on the knees.
Keep the spine and head straight.
Bring the awareness to the whole body and become steady and relaxed.
While slowly inhaling, raise the arms above the head, synchronizing the movement of arms and breath. Keep the arms shoulder-width apart.
Exhale slowly and bend the trunk forward bringing the chest to rest on the thighs and the forehead to the floor in front of the knees.
The arms remain outstretched in front of the body and the palms and elbows are resting on the floor.
Breathe normally, holding the posture for 10 seconds.
Inhale while returning slowly back to the upright position with arms stretched over the head.
Repeat up to 10 times.
After inhaling and returning to the upright position, exhale and bring the hands back to rest on the knees.
The breath should be slow and coordinated with the physical movements.
Concentration may be focused on manipura chakra, the solar plexus, or the natural breath.

Benefits: This asana (and variation 1) is very effective for toning the pelvic muscles, relaxing the sciatic nerves and regulating the functioning of the adrenal glands. Shashankasana helps relieve constipation, sciatica and anger. It is also a very effective asana for preventing an underdeveloped pelvis, and is beneficial for removing sexual disorders in general.

Variation 1: Sit in vajrasana and hold the right wrist with the left hand behind the back.
Become aware of the whole body and become relaxed and steady.
Inhale slowly and deeply.
While exhaling slowly bend the body forward, bringing the chest to rest on the thighs and the forehead to the floor in front of the knees.
Breathe normally while maintaining the position for about 10 seconds.
Inhale deeply and slowly raise the body to the upright position.
Repeat up to 10 times.

Variation 2: Sit in vajrasana and place the fists in front of the lower abdomen.
Let the little fingers of the fists rest on the lap.
Inhale deeply.
While exhaling slowly bend the body forward to rest the chest on the thighs and the forehead to the floor in front of the knees. Breathe normally while holding the posture for about 10 seconds.

Inhale while returning to the upright position.

Repeat up to 10 times.

For greater comfort and easier execution, overweight persons can place the hands flat on the abdomen.

Benefits: This variation massages and improves the efficiency of the intestines and digestive organs and is especially recommended for anyone suffering from constipation and excessive wind.

Pawanmuktasana 3

ENERGIZING ASANAS

These asanas are also combined with breathing, synchronization of movements and breath. They are called shakti bandha, or energy releasing asanas.

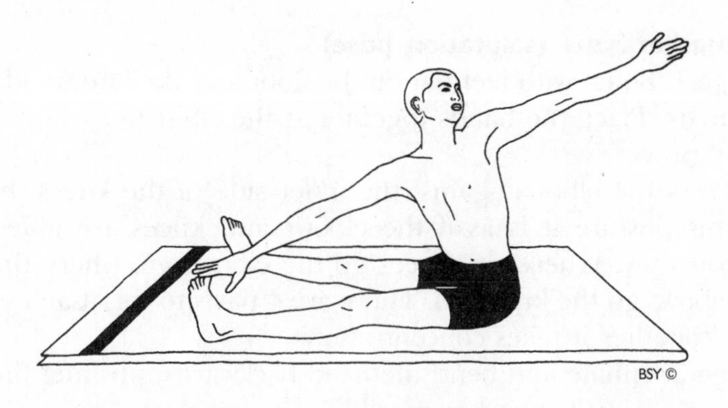

Gayatmak Meru Vakrasana (dynamic spinal twist)

Sit with both legs outstretched.
Separate the legs as wide apart as is comfortable.
Raise the arms straight out to the sides, twist the upper body and reach for the left toes with the right hand.
The left hand is stretched out behind the back and the head is turned to look at the outstretched left hand.
Close the eyes and feel the body.
Open the eyes and slowly twist the upper body back to the front and then to the other side.

Touch the right toes with the left hand and stretch the right hand behind the back. The head is turned to look at the outstretched right hand.
Again close the eyes and feel the whole body. This is one round. At the beginning, the exercise is done slowly, then the speed is gradually increased.
Do at least 10 rounds.
Exhale as you twist; inhale as you return to the centre.

Precautions: People suffering from high blood pressure or slipped disc should not practise this asana.

Benefits: This asana is not only beneficial for reducing the waistline and keeping the lateral movements of the spinal cord supple, but when practised with a little speed it stimulates and massages the abdominal organs and helps remove sluggishness and constipation.

Namaskarasana (salutation pose)

Stage 1: Squat with feet flat on the floor and the knees wide apart. Place the hands together at the chest in a gesture of prayer.
Press the elbows against the inner side of the knees. In this posture it is as if the elbows and knees are glued together. Where the knees go the elbows go, where the elbows go the knees go. There are 4 parts to this asana so altogether it takes concentration.

Stage 2: Inhale and bend the head backwards, pushing the knees as wide apart as possible.

Stage 3: Exhale while lowering the chin to the chest, and straightening the arms directly in front of the body.
At the same time push the upper arms in with the knees.

Stage 4: Inhale while raising the head and chin and pushing the knees wide apart with the elbows.
Bring the hands to the chest, palms together in prayer position, as in stage one.

Stage 5: Exhale and lower the head and chin back down to the chest.
Practise 5 to 8 rounds.

Benefits: This practice has a very powerful effect on the nerves of the thighs, knees, shoulders, arms and neck. It also increases flexibility in the hips. When practised in 4 stages it helps to develop concentration and awareness of body and breath moving in harmony.

Vayu Nishkasana (wind releasing pose)

Squat with both feet flat on the floor, 60 cm apart.
If the heels will not touch the floor then place a blanket or pillow under them so that the whole foot is taking the body weight, not just the toes.
Place the fingers under the feet from the inside so that the palms are under the arches, with the back of the hands resting on the floor. The elbows should press against the inner sides of the knees.
Inhale and raise the head.
Exhale, while straightening the legs, raising the buttocks, and bringing the head forward towards the knees.

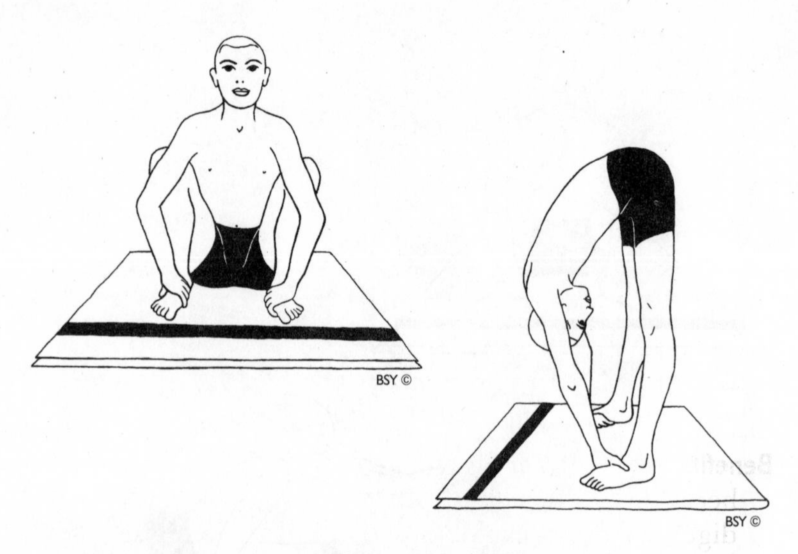

Maintain the position for a few seconds.
Inhale and return to the starting position.
Practise up to 8 times slowly and with great control and awareness.

Precautions: People with high blood pressure, sciatica or slipped disc should not practise this asana.

Benefits: This asana is beneficial for the nerves and muscles of the thighs, knees, shoulders, arms and neck. It stretches the hamstrings and promotes flexibility of the knee and hip joints.

Udarakarshanasana (abdominal stretch pose)

Squat with both feet flat on the floor and the hands on the knees.
Bring the right knee to the ground near the left foot while turning the trunk as much as possible to the left.
Look behind the body, and keep the hands on the knees.
Return to the starting position.
Repeat the same procedure twisting the body in the opposite direction.
Twist the body up to 10 times each way.
Inhale in the starting position, exhale turning to the side.

Benefits: This is a very useful asana for abdominal ailments because it alternately compresses and stretches the digestive organs and muscles. Constipation sufferers should practise it regularly.

Practice note: This is one of the asanas practised during shankhaprakshalana for cleaning the intestines and stomach.

Utthanasana (squat and rise pose)

Stand with the feet about 1 metre apart.

Turn the toes out to the sides.

Interlock the fingers in front of the abdomen and allow the arms to hang freely.

Stage 1: Slowly bend the knees and lower the buttocks about 20 cm.

Straighten the knees and return to the upright position.

Stage 2: Bend the knees and descend about half a metre.

Again return to the upright position.

Stage 3: Bend the knees and descend again until the hands are about 30 cms from the floor. Make sure that the spinal column is kept straight and the buttocks tucked in.

Return to the upright position.

Stage 4: Finally, lower the buttocks until the hands rest on or near the floor. Try not to bend forward.

Return to the upright position.

Repeat 5 to 10 times.

Breathing: Exhale while lowering, inhale while rising.

Benefits: This exercise strengthens the muscles of the middle of the back, pelvis and uterus, and also the inner thighs, knees and ankles. It helps encourage correct posture.

Saithalyasana (animal relaxation pose)

Sit in the base position.

Bend the right knee and place the sole of the foot against the inside left thigh.

Bend the left knee and place the heel to the outside of the left buttock.

Inhale and raise both hands slowly above the head.

While exhaling slowly bend forward over the right knee, bringing the forehead to the floor. Retain the position for about 1 minute, breathing normally and rhythmically.

Inhale while raising the arms and body, exhale and lower the hands to the right knee.

Practise 5 times on the right side, then reverse the position of the legs and repeat 5 times on the left side.

19

Eye Exercises

The following exercises can remove and prevent most eye diseases, both muscular and optical, if they are practised with patience and perseverance. Many people who have done these exercises over a long period of time have discarded their spectacles. Aldous Huxley was one such person.

After each of the exercises, the eyes should be closed and rested for at least half a minute. The more often the exercises are done the better; however, if there is lack of time in the daily program then the whole series performed once in the morning and once in the evening will suffice. If this is the case, there is extra reason to do the exercises with maximum dedication and awareness.

Exercise 1: Palming

Sit quietly with the eyes closed and face the sun if possible.

Rub the palms of the hands together vigorously until they become hot.

Place the palms gently over the eyelids.

Feel that warmth and energy is being transmitted from your hands into the eyes.

Remain in this position until the heat from the palms has been absorbed by the eyes. Keep the eyes closed.
Repeat the exercise at least 3 times.

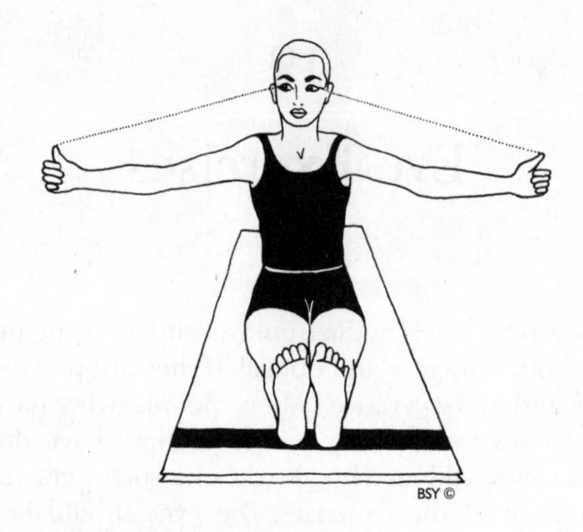

Exercise 2: Sideways viewing

Assume the base position.
Raise the arms out to the sides at shoulder level, keeping them straight, and point the thumbs upwards.
Without moving the head sideways, focus the eyes in the following sequence one after the other:

a) left thumb
b) space between the eyebrows (bhrumadhya)
c) right thumb
d) space between the eyebrows
e) left thumb

Repeat this cycle 15 to 20 times, and then close and rest the eyes. Palming may be performed several times.

Exercise 3: Front and sideways viewing

Sit in the base position as in exercise 2 but place the left fist on the left knee so that the thumb points upwards. Hold the right thumb to the right of the body, slightly above shoulder level.

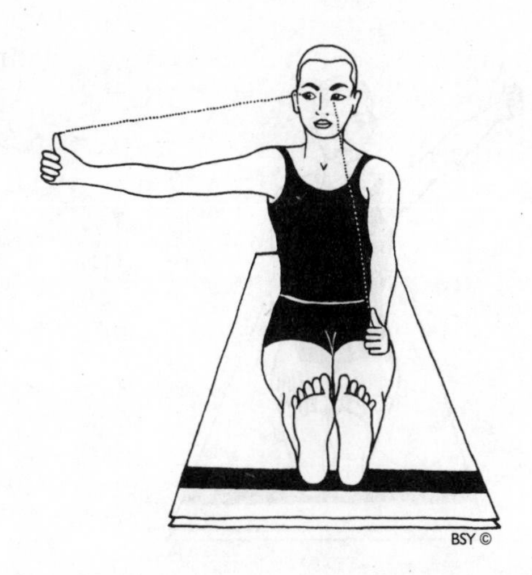

Without moving the head, focus the eyes first on the left thumb, then on the right thumb and then return to the left thumb and repeat.

Repeat this process 15 to 20 times.

Now close the eyes and rest, continuing to practise the technique mentally.

Repeat the same procedure with the right fist resting on the right knee and the left hand extended to the side just above shoulder level.

Finally close and rest the eyes.

Palming may be performed several times.

Exercise 4: Rotational viewing

Maintain the same body position as before, but place the left hand on the left knee and hold the right fist above the right leg.

The right thumb should point upwards and the right arm must be straight.

Slowly make a large circular movement with the right arm moving to the right, then upwards, curving to the left of the body and finally returning to the starting position.

During this movement keep your eyes focused on the thumb without moving the head.

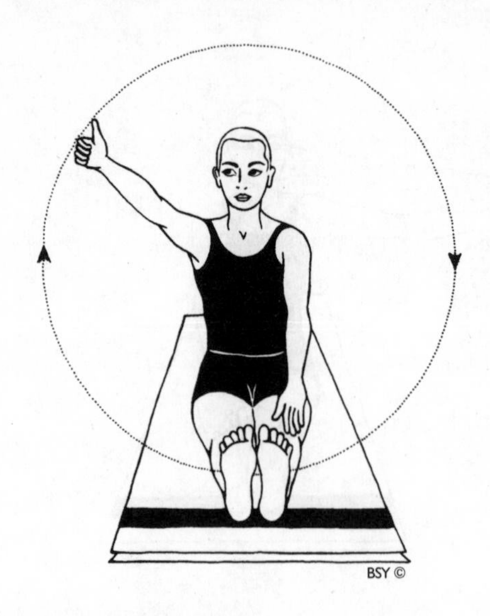

Perform 5 times clockwise and 5 times anti-clockwise.
Repeat with the left thumb.
Finally close and rest the eyes.
Palming may be performed several times.

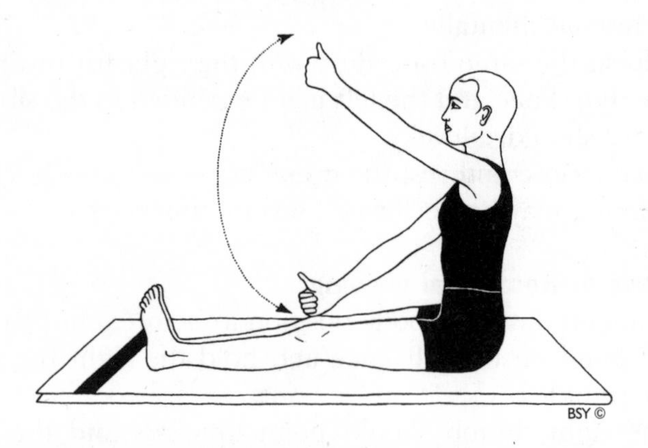

Exercise 5: Up and down viewing

Assume the base position and place both fists on the knees, with both thumbs pointing upwards.

Keeping the arms straight and the head motionless, slowly raise the right thumb, while following the motion of the thumb with the eyes.

On reaching the highest elevation slowly return to the starting position, keeping the eyes focused on the thumb all the time.
Practise the same movement with the left hand.
Repeat 5 times with each thumb.
Finally close and rest the eyes.
Palming may be performed several times.

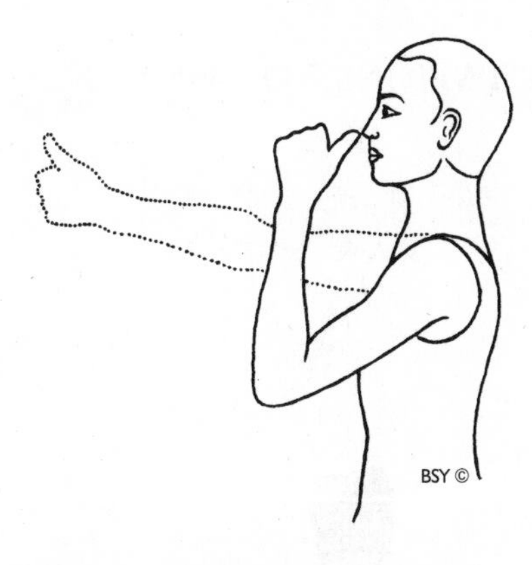

Exercise 6: Near and distant viewing

Maintain the same body position as before, relaxing the hands on the knees or the thighs.
Focus the eyes on the nosetip, then focus them on a distant object. Focus on the nosetip again.
Repeat this process 10 to 20 times.
Afterwards close the eyes and relax.
Palming may be performed.

Benefits: These exercises relax, revitalize and recharge the optic nerves.

20

Surya Namaskara

SALUTATIONS TO THE SUN

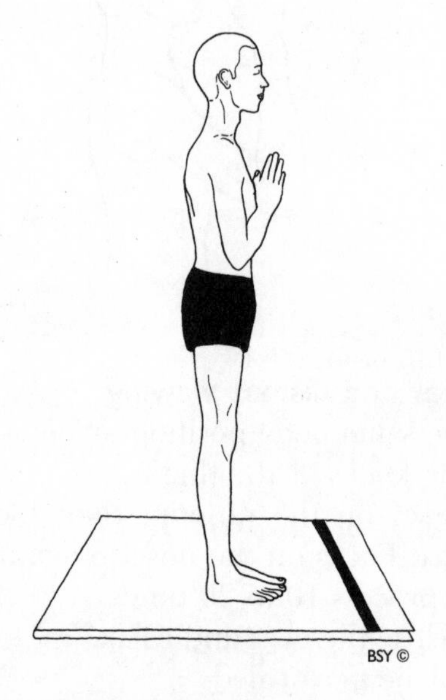

Position 1: Pranamasana (prayer pose)

Face the sun if possible.

Stand erect with feet together, palms together resting on the centre of the chest, arms relaxed against the body.

Breathe in and out with awareness until the breath is normal.

The whole body should be completely relaxed, spinal column straight but not rigid.

Benefits: This asana establishes a state of concentration, calmness and awareness of the practice being performed.

Position 2

Position 3

Position 2: Hasta Utthanasana (raised arms pose)

Inhale deeply while slowly raising the arms above the head.

Keep the arms separated, shoulder width apart.

Tilt the pelvis while arching the back and bending the head back as far as is comfortable. The spinal column is arched slightly in the beginning. The amount of the arch can increase with practice.

Benefits: This asana stretches all the abdominal organs fully, exercises the arms and shoulders, tones the spinal cord and opens up the lungs.

Position 3: Padahastasana (hand to foot pose)

Exhale deeply while slowly bending forward, keeping the knees straight. Place the fingers or palms of the hands beside the toes on the floor.

Try to touch the knees with the forehead. The spinal column is bent forward at the hip joints.

Initially bend forward only as far as is comfortable. With practice it will come easily.

Benefits: This asana aids in preventing, relieving and eliminating stomach ailments. It reduces surplus abdominal fat, improves digestion, eliminates constipation, improves circulation and keeps the spine supple.

Position 4: Ashwa Sanchalanasana (equestrian pose)

Keep the palms of the hands or the fingertips on the floor beside the feet.

Inhale deeply while slowly stretching the right leg back as far as is possible, and bending the left knee.

The right toe and knee touch the floor. Arch the back and look up.

The spinal column is once again arched and the chin should be raised as high as is possible. After some practice the spinal arch will become very pronounced.

Benefits: This asana tones the abdominal muscles, strengthens the muscles of the thighs and legs and induces balance in the nervous system.

Position 5: Parvatasana (mountain pose)

Exhale deeply while slowly stretching the right leg back and placing it beside the left leg.

At the same time raise the buttocks and lower the head between the arms, so that the back and legs form two sides of a triangle.

The legs and arms should be straight in the final position.

Try to keep the heels on the ground and bring the head towards the knees.

This is often called the dog pose.

Benefits: This asana strengthens the nerves and muscles of the arms and legs, exercises the spine and stimulates circulation especially in the upper spine. It is an inverted posture which can be practised by those who are unable to do sirshasana, the headstand pose, due to myopia.

Position 6: Ashtanga Namaskara (salute with 8 limbs)

Slowly lower the knees to the floor, then the chest and finally the chin.

In the final position only the toes, knees, chest, hands and chin touch the floor.

The spinal column is arched slightly in this balancing pose. With practise, it should be possible to touch the knees, chest and chin to the floor at the same time.

Exhale and inhale as much as is necessary in this position, or retain the breath outside.

Benefits: This asana tones the shoulders and neck muscles, strengthens leg and arm muscles and develops the chest.

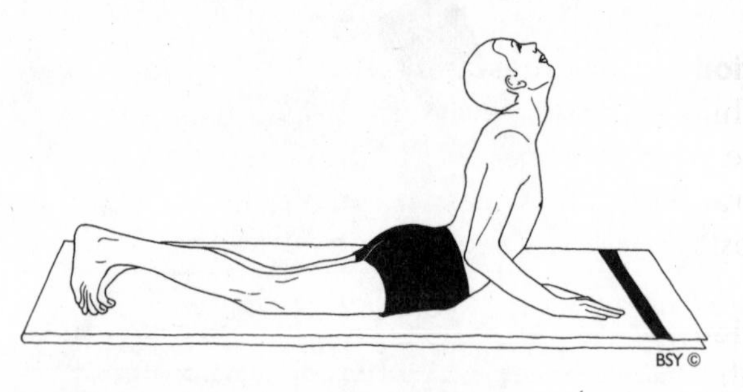

Position 7: Bhujangasana (cobra pose)

While inhaling deeply slowly lower the buttocks and hips to the floor.

Straighten the elbows, arch the back and push the chest forward into the cobra pose.

Bend the head back.

Benefits: As given for ashtanga namaskara. Also, in this asana the abdominal stretch helps to squeeze stagnant blood from the abdominal organs and encourage a flow of fresh blood. This pose is useful for all stomach ailments, including indigestion and constipation. The arching of the back keeps the spine supple, improves circulation and revitalizes most important spinal nerves. It also has a balancing effect on many hormones.

Position 8: Parvatasana (mountain pose)

Relax the arch and exhale deeply, while slowly raising the buttocks and lowering the heels to the floor.

The hands and feet do not move from position 7.

The body should look like a triangle as in position 5 with the chin tucked in close to the chest.

Position 9: Ashwa Sanchalanasana (equestrian pose)

While inhaling deeply slowly bring the left foot forward between the two hands.

At the same time, lower the right knee down to the floor and push the pelvis forward.

Arch the back and look up, with the chin as high as possible. This is the same as position 4.

Position 10: Padahastasana (hand to foot pose)

While exhaling slowly bring the left foot forward next to the right foot.

Straighten the knees and bring the forehead as close as possible to the knees without straining, as in position 3.

Position 11: Hasta Utthanasana (raised arms pose)

Inhale deeply while slowly raising the body from the hip and stretching the arms overhead, shoulder width apart. Tilt the pelvis then arch the back, and raise the chin as high as possible, as in position 2.

Position 12: Pranamasana (prayer pose)

Exhale while bringing the palms together in front of the chest, standing erect as in position 1.

Relax the body and watch the breath return to normal.

Positions 13–24: Positions 1–12 constitute half a round. The second half round consists of the same twelve positions. The only difference is in position 16 where the left leg is taken back, and in position 21 where the right foot is brought forward between the hands. Start the second half round when the heartbeat and breath have returned to normal. When a number of full rounds have been completed, lie in shavasana to rest and relax the body and breath.

Benefits: When one performs surya namaskara synchronizing the physical movements with the breath, all the muscles, joints and major internal organs are stimulated and balanced. It is for this reason that surya namaskara is an ideal practice for people with only a limited amount of time to devote to the practice of asana and pranayama.

Surya namaskara also influences the pineal gland and the hypothalamus, helping to prevent pineal degeneration and calcification. This balances the transition period between childhood and adolescence in growing children.

21

Chandra Namaskara

SALUTATIONS TO THE MOON

Chandra namaskara is very much like surya namaskara and the benefits are similar. However, in chandra namaskara the sequence can be taught in three different ways.

Variation 1: Beginners practice

Position 1: Vajrasana

Sit in vajrasana with palms together in front of the chest.

Position 2: Marjariasana (cat pose)

Then move into marjariasana, the cat pose, by lifting the buttocks and raising the body up on the knees.

Both palms are placed flat on the floor, about shoulder width apart, directly under the shoulders.

Position 2

Position 3: Ardha Chandrasana (half moon pose)

Slowly move the left foot forward and place it between the hands near the inside of the left hand.

Arch the back, raise the chin and look up.

Bring the palms together again and stretch the arms up above the head. If this is too difficult, separate the hands and arms a little.

From the tips of the fingers to the tips of the toes of the right foot looks like a crescent moon.

Position 3

Position 4

Relax the arch while bringing the palms back down to the floor on either side of the left foot.

Bring the left knee back to the floor beside the right knee so that you are once again in marjariasana.

Position 4

Position 5

Sit back down on the heels and bring the palms together, back to rest in front of the chest, as in position 1.

Positions 6–10: The second half of the round differs in position 18 where the right foot is brought forward between the hands.

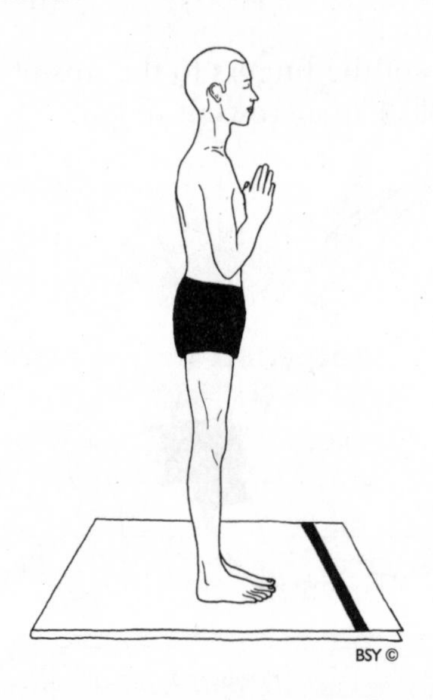

Variation 2: Ardha Chandra Namaskara (salutations to the half moon)

Position 1: Pranamasana (prayer pose)

Stand erect with the legs together, palms together in front of the chest, arms relaxed against the body.

Breathe in and out until the breath is normal.
The spinal column is straight but not rigid.
The whole body is completely relaxed.

Position 2 Position 3

Position 2: Hasta Utthanasana (raised arms pose)

Inhale deeply while slowly raising the arms, tilt the pelvis while arching the back and bend the head back.
The spinal column is arched slightly in the beginning.
Ultimately, after intensive practise, the amount of arch here can be so great that the body looks like a crescent moon.

Position 3: Padahastasana (hand to foot pose)

Exhale deeply while slowly bending forward at the hip joints, with straight legs until the head touches the knees.
Place the hands beside the feet on the floor.
In the beginning go as close to the floor as possible with the hands but do not bend the knees.

Position 4: Ardha Chandrasana (half moon pose)

Inhale deeply while slowly moving the right leg back, away from the body in a backward stretch, though not too far back. The top of the right foot, lower leg and knee rest on the floor.

Arch the back and look up, raising the chin as high as possible.

Bring the palms together, then stretch the arms over the head.

If this proves too difficult separate the hands and arms.

From the fingertips to the tips of the toes there should be an appearance of a crescent moon.

Position 5: Padahastasana (hand to foot pose)

Relax the arch and bring the hands back to the floor beside the left foot.

Exhale while bringing the right foot back between the hands beside the left foot.

Legs are straight and forehead is brought to the knees, as in position 3.

Position 6: Hasta Utthanasana (raised arms pose)

Inhale deeply while slowly raising the arms overhead.

Arch the back and raise the chin as high as possible, as in position 2.

Position 7: Pranamasana (prayer pose)

Exhale while bringing the palms together in front of the chest, standing erect as in position 1.

Relax the body.

Be aware of the natural breath until it is normal again.

Then begin the second half of the round.

Positions 8–14: The second half of the round differs in that in position 11 the left foot is stretched backwards. Make sure the breath and heartbeat are not too fast before beginning the second half of the round.

Variation 3: Poorna Chandra Namaskara (salutations to the full moon)

Practice note: Poorna chandra namaskara is closer to surya namaskara than variations 1 and 2. In the full version of chandra namaskara there are 14 positions relating to the 14 phases of the moon, whereas surya namaskara has 12 positions which relate to the 12 solar months or zodiac signs.

Positions 1–4 are the same as surya namaskara. Position 5 is ardha chandrasana with the arms raised. Positions 6–10 are the same as positions 5–9 of surya namaskara. Position 11 is again ardha chandrasana with raised arms. Positions 12–14 are the same as positions 10–12 of surya namaskara. The second half of the round is performed by placing the opposite leg back in position 4 and bringing the opposite leg forward in position 10.

22

Warrior Sequence

The warrior sequence has three variations, each one demanding more of a stretch and, of course, more control than the one before.

Position 1

Position 2

Variation 1: Beginner's practice

Position 1: Stand erect with the feet about a metre apart. Inhale, while placing the palms together in front of the chest.

Position 2

Exhale while stretching the arms out to the sides at shoulder height.

Position 3

Inhale while bringing the palms of the outstretched arms together above the head.

Position 3

Position 4

Position 4

Hold the breath in while twisting the body towards the right so that the right leg is in front of the left leg.
The right foot is turned to the right so it is at right angles to the left foot.

Position 5

Exhale while bending the right knee and bring the outstretched arms to shoulder level in front of the body, keeping the palms together.
Keep the back straight and the left foot flat on the floor.

Position 6

Hold the breath out while straightening the right knee and bringing the arms back overhead, palms together as in position 4.

Position 7

Inhale while turning the body to face the front again, as in position 3.

Position 8

Exhale, while bringing the arms back down to shoulder height, outstretched to each side of the body, as shown in position 2.

Position 9

Inhale, while bringing the palms together to rest against the chest as in position 1.

Positions 10–18: Each sequence must be practised to one side of the body and then to the other. Note that in the second half of the round, in position 13 the body is turned towards the left, and in position 14 the left knee is bent.

Variation 2: Intermediate practice

Positions 1–9: Positions 1 to 4 remain the same as in variation 1. Position 5 becomes a little more difficult. After position 5 come back the same way as in variation 1.

Position 5

Exhale while bending the right knee and bring the chest to rest on the right thigh.

The palms are still together and the fingertips are brought to the floor in front of the right foot, with the knee between the arms.

Remember that the spine must be kept straight and the left foot flat on the floor.

Positions 10–18: As in the previous variation both sides of the body should be exercised to complete the round, so repeat to the left side.

Always make sure that the body and breath are relaxed before starting the second half round.

Variation 3: Advanced practice

Positions 1–9: This variation is again similar to the previous two, except for position 5 which becomes more difficult. After position 5 return as in variations 1 and 2.

Position 5

Exhale while bending the right knee and bending forward. Now the right knee is not between the arms but the elbows are bent and brought to the ground on the inside of the right foot. The forehead comes down to the hands. It is very important to keep the left foot flat on the floor.

Positions 10–18: As in the previous variations, in position 13 of the second half of the round the body is turned towards the left, so that in position 14 the left knee is bent and the body is stretched forward to the left side.

Benefits: This sequence develops strong leg muscles and flexibility of the spinal column. It develops balance and concentration.

Practice note: Note that in variations 1 and 2 the back is straight in position 5, and in each variation the trailing foot in position 5 is kept flat on the floor. Try not to rest the weight on the arms in position 5 of variation 3.

As with all dynamic sequences, and indeed most asanas, it is important to synchronize the length of the breath with the time it takes to do the movement, i.e., start the breath as you start the movement. This will lead to graceful and effortless asana practice and will carry through into daily life in the form of poise and economy of energy.

23

Relaxation Asanas

Shavasana (corpse pose)

Lie on the back with the feet comfortably apart.

The spinal column is straight but not rigid and the arms rest on the floor about 15 cm away from the body with the palms up.

The head is in line with the spine and the eyes and mouth are gently closed.

Let the whole body relax completely so that it feels heavy like a statue.

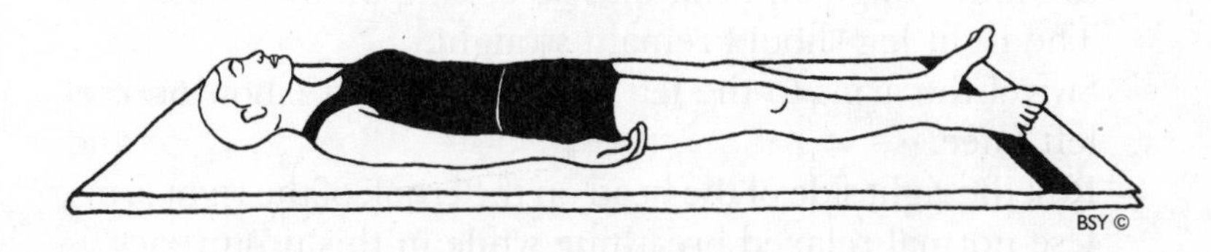

Do not move any part of the body. Become aware of the breath and let it become rhythmic and natural.

Begin to count the breaths. The natural breath flowing in and then out is one round of the breath. This may be repeated as long as desired, or one may choose to do 21 rounds, or any particular number of rounds.

Remember it is the natural breathing rhythm that one is counting.

If it relaxes and becomes deeper, that too is the natural breathing rhythm.

Benefits: This asana relaxes the whole psychophysiological system. Ideally it should be practised before, during and after an asana session; after a dynamic pose like surya namaskara; before sleeping; and when one is physically and mentally tired.

When practised with awareness, it will calm a nervous and tense mind.

Matsya Kridasana (flapping fish pose)

Lie on the stomach with fingers interlocked under the right cheek.

Bend the left knee and bring it up close to the ribs, with the inner thigh and calf muscle resting on the floor.

The right leg should remain straight.

Swivel the arms to the left and rest the left elbow on the left knee.

Rest the right side of the head on the crook of the right arm.

Use normal relaxed breathing while in this posture.

Relax in the final pose and, after some time, change sides.

Benefits: This is an excellent rest pose and can be used for sleeping. It redistributes waistline fat deposits and stimulates digestive peristalsis by stretching the intestines, which helps to relieve constipation.

This practice also relieves sciatic pain by relaxing the muscles in the legs and altering the angles of stress on the sciatic nerves.

Makarasana (crocodile pose)

Lie on the stomach. Raise the head and shoulders and rest the chin in the palms of the hands with the elbows placed on the floor.

Let the heels flop outwards.

Benefits: This is an easy and effective posture for those suffering from slipped disc, sciatica, lower back pain or any other spinal disorder. For best results one should remain in this position for extended lengths of time. Asthmatics and people with lung ailments should practise this simple asana regularly with breath awareness as it allows more air to enter the lungs.

24

Animal Asanas

Matsyasana (fish pose)

Simple variation: Lie flat in shavasana with the arms resting on the floor by the sides.

Arch the back, press against the floor with the lower arms and bring the top of the head to rest on the floor.

The weight of the body rests on the outstretched legs, buttocks and top of the head.

Place both palms on the thighs.

Hold for a short time.

To release the pose, bring the hands back down to the floor, relax the arch and return to shavasana.

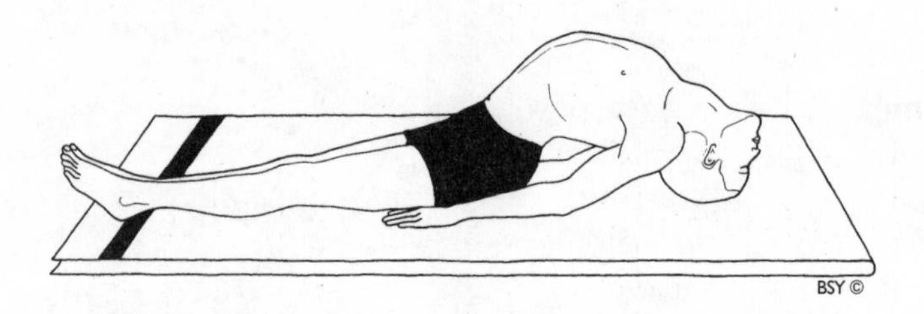

Advanced variation: Sit in padmasana. Carefully bend backward, supporting the body with the arms and elbows, until the crown of the head touches the floor.

Hold the big toes and rest the elbows on the floor.

Keep the back well arched.

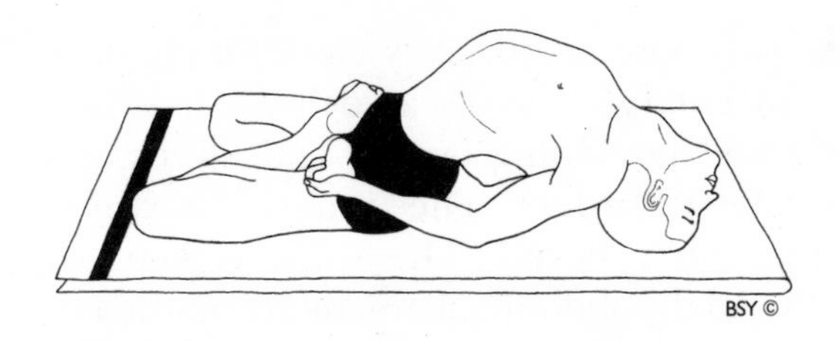

Relax the whole body, allowing the head, buttocks and legs to support the body.

To return to the starting position place the palms on the floor and push on the forearms.

Benefits: This posture stretches the intestines and abdominal organs thoroughly and expands the lungs. It is recommended where there is a tendency to bronchial contractions or asthma, lung diseases, bronchitis etc.

Bhujangasana (cobra pose)

Lie flat on the stomach, legs straight, feet together.

Place the palms of the hands flat on the floor slightly to the sides of the shoulders.

Rest the forehead on the floor.

Inhaling, slowly raise the head, neck and shoulders. Straighten the elbows and raise the trunk as high as possible, so that the back is arched to the maximum and the chin raised as high as possible.

Hold the breath in for a short time.

Lower the body while exhaling.

Benefits: This pose is especially good for children suffering from an enlarged or diseased liver. It is beneficial for toning the developing ovaries and uterus and relieving menstrual disorders. The appetite is stimulated and constipation relieved. The spine is kept supple and healthy. All the abdominal organs are massaged, especially the liver and kidneys. It relocates slipped discs and removes backache.

Tiryaka Bhujangasana (twisting cobra pose)

Inhaling, assume the final pose of bhujangasana, with the legs about half a metre apart, toes turned under, heels pointing upwards.

The head should face forward.

Holding the breath in, twist the head and upper part of the trunk, and look over the left shoulder at the heel of the right foot.

Bring the head back to the front.

Twist to the right side, looking over the shoulder at the left heel.

Return to the centre and lower the body to the floor while exhaling.

Benefits: This exercise gives all the benefits of bhujangasana but also aids in promoting lateral movements of the spinal cord.

Children enjoy imagining the cobra raising his head and slowly looking around on either side.

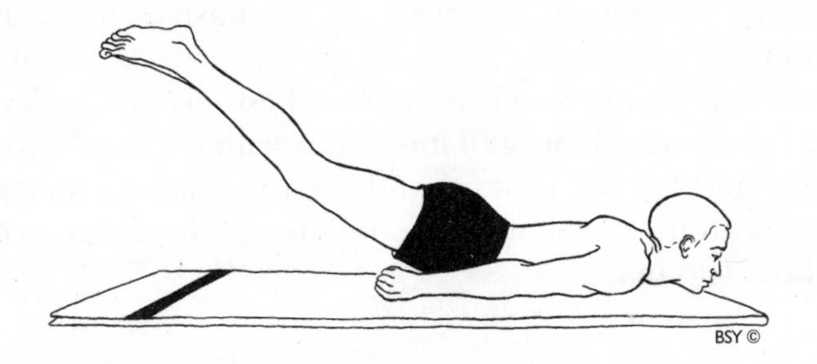

Shalabhasana (locust pose)

Lie flat on the stomach with the hands under the thighs, palms down or hands clenched.

Inhale, retain the breath and raise the left leg as high as possible, keeping the knee straight.

Exhale while lowering the leg to the floor.

Repeat the same movement with the right leg.

Inhale, retain the breath inside and slowly raise both legs as high as possible, keeping them straight.

Keep the trunk on the floor by pressing the arms and hands against the floor.

Maintain this position for five to thirty seconds.

Exhale while slowly lowering the legs back to the starting position.

Benefits: This asana strengthens the lower back and pelvic organs, and tones the sciatic nerves, relieving backache, mild sciatica and slipped disc.

It also tones and balances the abdominal organs, the liver, pancreas and kidneys. It aids in the relief and elimination of diseases of the stomach and bowels, and stimulates the appetite.

Shashank Bhujangasana (striking cobra pose)

Sit in vajrasana.

Inhale deeply while slowly raising the arms above the head.

Exhaling, slowly lower the chest to the thighs and forehead to the floor in front of the knees. Keep the outstretched arms about shoulder width apart with the palms and

elbows resting on the floor as in shashankasana, the moon or hare pose.
Inhaling deeply, slowly move the chest forward, sliding it just above the floor until it is in line with the hands. Move the chest further forward and then upward, as the arms straighten, and lower the pelvis to the floor, as in bhujangasana.

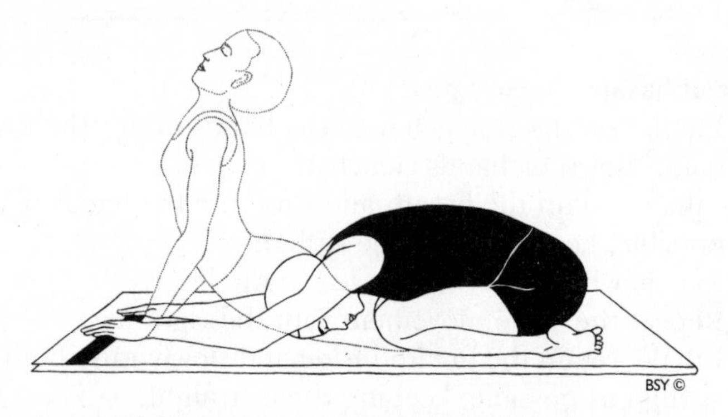

In the final position, the arms should be straight, the back arched and the chin held as high as possible.
The navel does not touch the floor.
Hold for a few seconds, retaining the breath.
Exhaling, slowly raise the buttocks, bend the knees and move backwards, keeping the arms straight, and return to shashankasana.
This is one round.
The palms of the hands remain in one spot throughout the movement from shashankasana to bhujangasana.
While inhaling move the chin and chest forward again into the cobra posture, hold, then while exhaling return to the moon pose.
This movement is repeated 7 times.
After the seventh cobra, exhale while returning to the moon pose, then inhale while sitting upright again, raising the arms over the head.
Exhale while slowly lowering the arms and rest the hands on the knees.

Benefits: This is a very good dynamic asana, combining both forward and backward movements of the spinal column. It aids sufferers of sciatica, slipped disc, general back pain and displaced ribs by stretching and massaging the entire back. It tones and improves the functioning of the liver, kidneys and other visceral organs. It gently tones the female reproductive organs, alleviates menstrual disorders and is an excellent post-natal asana, strengthening and tightening the abdominal and pelvic region.

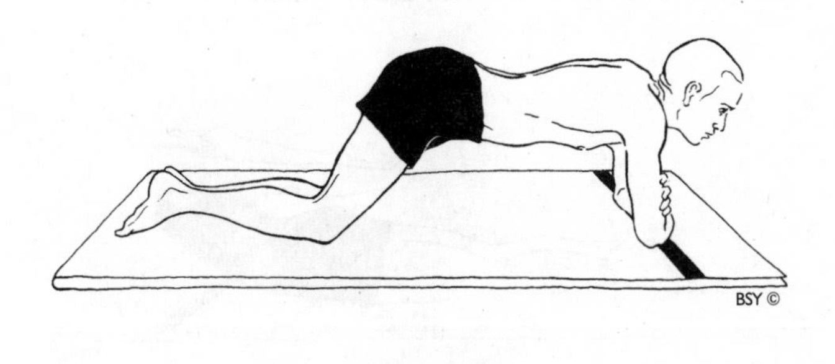

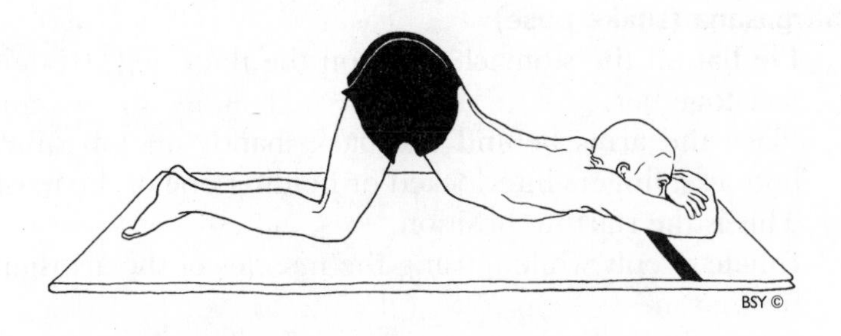

Utthan Pristhasana (lizard pose)

Lie on the stomach with the arms crossed under the lower chest, hands holding the upper arms (biceps).

The legs are slightly separated, toes stretched out, head facing forwards, body weight resting on the forearms.

The elbows should not move during the practice.

Inhaling, raise the trunk and buttocks so that the body is supported by the knees and lower arms.

Exhaling, bend the knees and stretch the torso backwards, placing the chin and chest on the floor behind the forearms.

Inhale while returning to the raised position and exhale while returning to the lying position.

This is one round.

Do up to 10 rounds.

Benefits: This asana is a good counterpose to forward bending asanas. It exercises and strengthens the diaphragm and tones the entire back, especially relieving tightness between the shoulder blades.

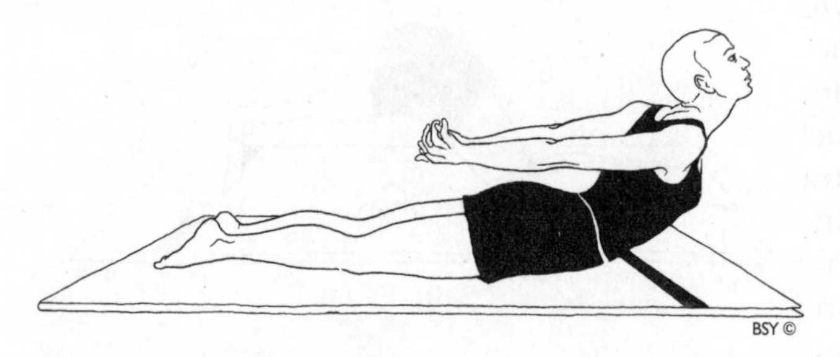

Sarpasana (snake pose)

Lie flat on the stomach, chin on the floor, legs straight, feet together.

Place the arms behind the back, hands on top of the buttocks, fingers interlocked or holding one of the wrists. This is the starting position.

Inhale deeply while tensing the muscles of the arms and back.

Using the lower back muscles, raise the chest as far as possible from the floor. Push the hands further back and raise the arms as high as possible. Imagine the arms are being pulled from behind.

Hold the breath in, then exhale while relaxing back down to the floor.

Benefits: Basically the same as for bhujangasana with increased influence on the chest. It is useful for asthmatics. It also helps to release blocked emotions.

Koormasana (tortoise pose)

Sit with the legs spread as wide apart as possible, with the feet on the floor and knees slightly bent.

While exhaling lean forward and insert the hands under the knees with the palms downward.

Slowly slide the arms under the legs, sideways and backwards.

Straighten the legs as far as possible.

Gradually move the body forward until the forehead or chin touches the floor between the legs.

Bring the chest close to the floor and clasp the hands behind the buttocks.

Breathe slowly and deeply in the final position.

The awareness is on relaxing the back and abdominal muscles.

Inhale while raising the knees and placing the feet flat on the floor, then release the hands and return to the sitting position.

Benefits: This asana should not be attempted by anyone with slipped disc, sciatica and chronic arthritis. It is good for removing excess fat from the abdomen, toning all the internal organs of the abdomen and the kidneys, as well as relieving ailments such as diabetes, flatulence and constipation.

It also encourages a flow of fresh blood to the spinal nerves and muscles and helps to remove chronic backache, headache and neckache.

Marjariasana (cat stretch pose)

Sit in vajrasana, raise the buttocks and rise up on the knees to a kneeling position.

Place both palms on the floor directly under the shoulders. The two arms and two thighs should look like the four legs of a cat. While inhaling deeply, slowly depress the back and abdomen towards the floor and raise the chin as high as possible. Then exhale deeply while slowly arching the spine up like a cat.

Pull the abdomen up towards the spine and tuck the chin down to the chest.

Repeat up to 10 times.

Benefits: This asana improves the flexibility of the neck, shoulders and spine. It gently tones the female reproductive system, relieving menstrual irregularities and leucorrhea. It may be practised at time of menstruation for relief from menstrual cramps. The benefits are enhanced if the stomach is contracted during relaxation.

Vyaghrasana (tiger pose)

Sit in vajrasana, move forward into the cat pose and look forward. Inhale, stretching the right leg backwards, parallel to the floor.

Bend the right knee and point the toes towards the head. Raise the chin as high as possible as if you want to touch the back of the head with the right toes.

While exhaling deeply, slowly bring the knee down under the body and bring the thigh against the chest.

Lower the chin to the chest so the nose touches the knee.

Inhale, raise the knee, point the toes towards the head and bring the chin up, then again exhale and bring the thigh to the chest and the nose to the knee.

Repeat up to 5 times, then practise with the left leg.

Benefits: This asana exercises the spine, relieves sciatica, tones the female reproductive organs, stretches the abdominal muscles and reduces excess fat on the hips and thighs.

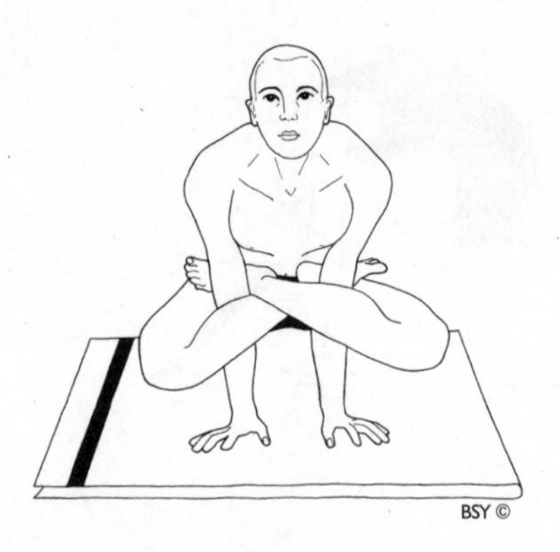

Kukkutasana (cockerel pose)

Sit in padmasana.

Insert the arms between the calves and the thighs.

Place the palms on the floor, fingers pointing forward.

Inhale, raise the body from the floor, balancing only on the hands.

Keep the back straight.

Hold for as long as is comfortable.

Exhale and lower the body back down to the floor.

Benefits: This posture strengthens the hands, arms and shoulder muscles, and helps develop the chest.

Practice note: The arms and wrists must be strong enough to support the body.

Baka Dhyanasana (patient crane pose)

Squat on the floor with the feet apart.

Rise onto the tiptoes and place the hands flat on the ground directly in front of the feet.

The elbows should be slightly bent.

Position the inside of the knees so that they touch the outside of the upper arms, as near as possible to the armpits.

Inhale while slowly leaning forward and lifting the feet off the floor, balancing only on the hands.

The knees should rest firmly on the upper arms. Bring the feet together.

Benefits: People with high blood pressure, heart disease or cerebral thrombosis should not attempt this asana. Regular practice of this pose steadies the nervous system and removes tension and anxiety. It strengthens the arms and wrists and develops a sense of balance. This asana requires nervous coordination more than muscular strength, although beginners may mistakenly believe the opposite.

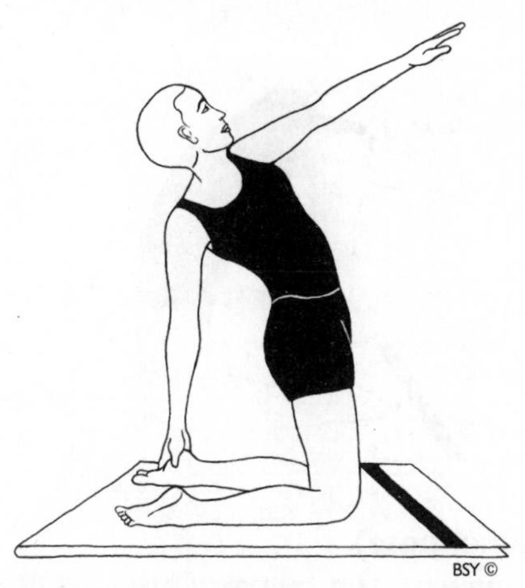

Ardha Ushtrasana (half camel pose)

Sit in vajrasana with the knees slightly apart.

Inhale while rising up on the knees and stretch the arms out to the sides.

Exhale while twisting the torso to the right, bend backwards and grasp the left heel with the right hand.

The left arm should be raised vertically over the head with the palm facing forward.
Gaze at the left hand.
Allow the upper body weight to rest on the left heel.
Inhale while raising the torso and return to the centred kneeling position.
Exhale while twisting the torso to the left.
If this proves difficult for some children they can try placing the right hand on the right heel and raising the left arm.
Then repeat to the opposite side.
Practise a maximum of 10 times on each side as a dynamic pose. As a static pose practise for 1 minute on each side.

Benefits: This backward bending pose may be practised as a counterpose for forward bending asanas such as shashankasana, paschimottanasana, etc. It is useful for stretching the stomach and intestines to eliminate constipation, and for relieving backache, lumbago and rounded back.

Ushtrasana (camel pose)

Sit in vajrasana with the feet and knees slightly apart.
Inhaling, stand on the knees.
Lean backward and place the hands on the heels while exhaling.
Push the abdomen forward, arch the back and tilt the head backwards, letting the body weight rest on the arms.
The thighs should be vertical.

Breathe normally in this position.
Return to the starting position, releasing the hands from the heels one at a time.

Benefits: This posture stretches the abdomen, relieves constipation and tones the abdominal viscera, including the liver, pancreas and kidneys. It aids in eliminating sluggishness of the liver, diseases of the stomach and intestines, and is beneficial for the reproductive system. The backward bend relieves backache, rounded back, lumbago and drooping shoulders. The stretch to the front of the neck helps to regulate the thyroid gland.

Gomukhasana (cow's face pose)

Sit with the legs outstretched.
Fold the left leg and place the heel beside the right buttock.
Fold the right leg over the top of the left leg so that the right heel is on the ground beside the left thigh.
The knees should lie one above the other.
Place the left arm behind the back and the right hand over the right shoulder and join the fingers of each hand behind the back.

Make the trunk erect, hold the head straight and close the eyes while placing the awareness at the top of the spinal cord at the pineal gland.

Then repeat with the opposite arm and leg.

Benefits: This asana aids in the elimination of diabetes, backache, stiff shoulders and neck, and sexual ailments. It stimulates the kidneys and so improves the purification process in the body. It alleviates sciatica and rheumatism and develops the chest.

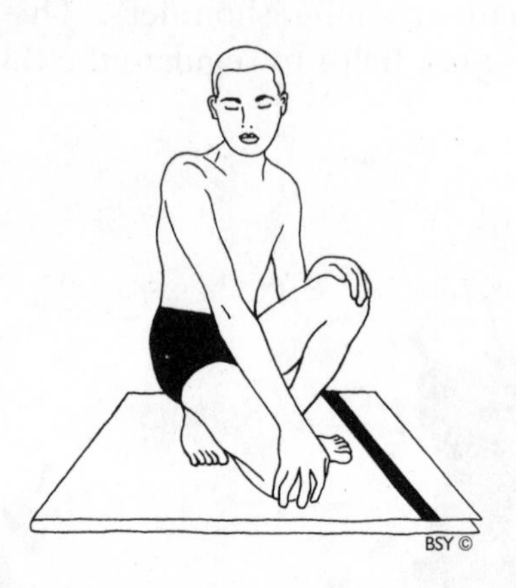

Kawa Chalasana (crow walking)

Squat on the floor with the feet apart and the buttocks above the heels.

Place the palms of the hands on the knees and begin to walk in this squatting position. One can either walk on the toes or on the feet; choose whichever is most difficult. Do this exercise for a short time without strain.

Benefits: This is a very good exercise to prepare the legs for meditation poses. It is also recommended for those children who suffer from poor blood circulation in the legs. Constipation sufferers will find this exercise useful. Drink 2 glasses of water and then do crow walking for one minute. Drink 2 more glasses of water and repeat the exercise. Repeat this 3 or 4 times, then the constipation should be relieved.

Variation: A variation of this pose is to touch the knee to the ground with each step. This causes the bottom to sway like a duck when it walks. Young children love practising this asana, especially when sound effects are added to the practice.

Bakasana (crane pose)

Stand erect with the feet together and arms raised above the head.

Bend the body at the hips and grasp the toes of the right foot with both hands.

Slowly raise the left leg behind as high as possible, bringing the forehead down towards the knee.

Do not bend the knee.

Lower the leg and return to the standing position.

Repeat on the other side.

Benefits: Bakasana improves blood circulation to the brain, strengthens the arms, wrists and leg muscles, relaxes the lower back and aids in the attainment of nervous coordination.

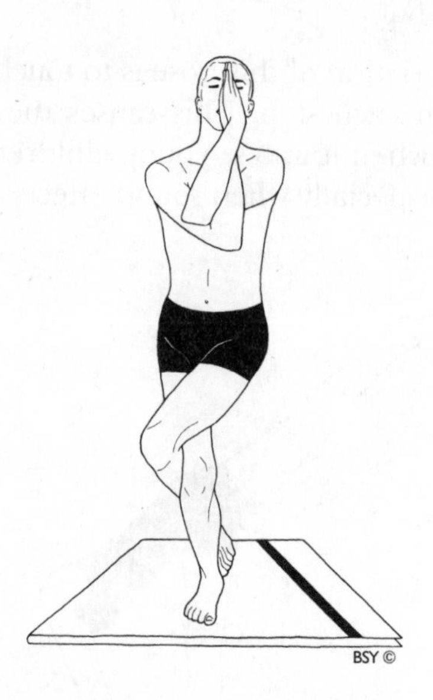

Garudasana (eagle pose)

From a standing position raise the right leg and twist it round the left leg.

The right thigh should be placed in front of the left thigh and the top of the right foot should rest on the calf of the left leg.

Interlace the arms in front of the chest, placing the palms together to resemble an eagle's beak.

Bend the left knee and lower the body until the right toe touches the floor.

Hold for as long as possible.

Return to a standing position and then repeat on the opposite side.

Benefits: The bones, muscles and nerves of the legs are strengthened. Balance and concentration are improved.

Poorna Titali Asana (full butterfly pose)

Sit with legs outstretched in front of the body.

Bend the knees and place the soles of the feet together, bringing the heels as close to the body as possible.

Interlock the fingers and place them under the feet.

Bring the knees down towards the ground and raise them up again.

The knees moving up and down should make the legs look like the wings of a butterfly in flight.

Benefits: This asana is very good for bringing mobility to the hip joints. Children usually find this asana very enjoyable but are not necessarily able to do the final pose, so its practice should be encouraged.

Simhasana (lion pose)

If possible, face the sun for healing purposes.

Sit in vajrasana with the knees about 45 cm apart.

Place the hands on the floor between the knees with the fingers pointing toward the body.

Then lean forward, resting the body on the arms with the elbows locked.

Inhale completely then tilt the head backwards, open the mouth and stretch out the tongue as far as possible, exposing both the tongue and throat to the rays of the sun.

While exhaling produce a clear, steady roaring sound, '*ahhh*'.

Benefits: This pose is especially recommended for children. It helps to cure diseased or swollen tonsils when practised facing the sun. Tension is removed from the chest and diaphragm. It is a good remedial aid against diseases of

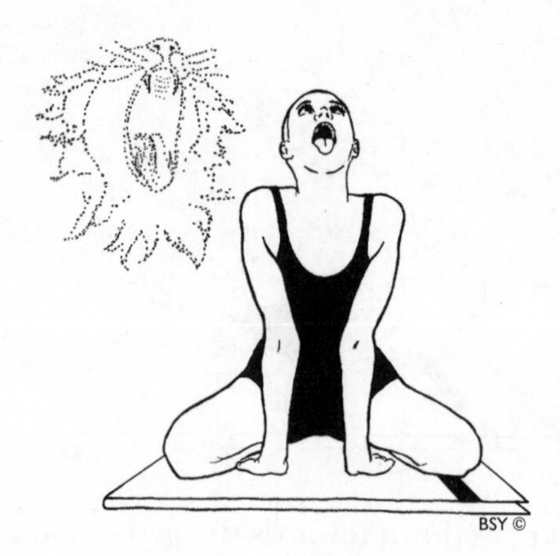

the throat, nose, ears, mouth or teeth. It is helpful in controlling stammering or stuttering. It develops a strong and beautiful voice.

Practice note: This asana is a great favourite with most children because it incorporates several enjoyable pastimes which are normally forbidden, such as sticking the tongue out and making a loud growling noise!

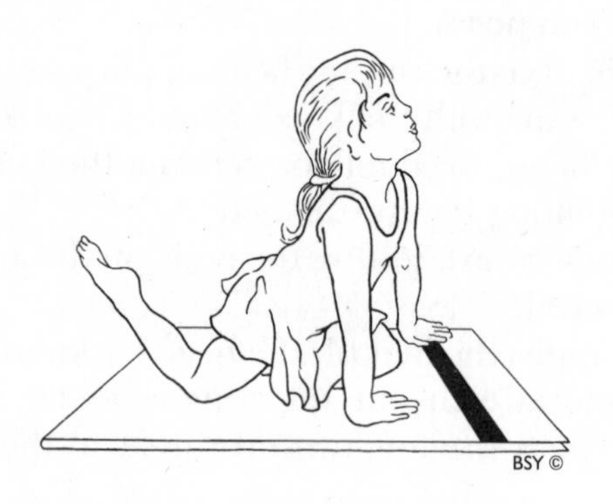

Variation: Leo the friendly lion

Sit in vajrasana with the knees together and the hands resting on the floor on each side of the knees.

Stretch the right leg out behind.

Tell the children that the lion is stretching his tail out behind him.

Then bend the right knee.
Now the lion is not feeling friendly and waves his tail from side to side.
The right foot is then moved from side to side.
Straighten the right knee then bend it under the body and assume vajrasana once again.
Practise the same movement with the left leg.

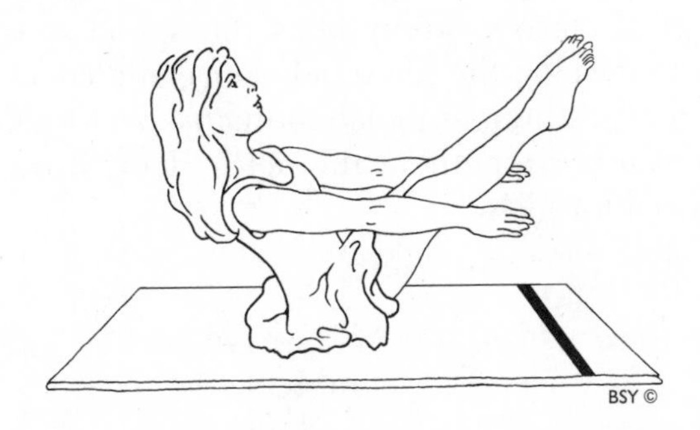

Vajroli Mudra (thunderbolt attitude, letter V or lapwing pose)

Simple variation: Sit in the base position with legs stretched out in front, palms on the floor beside the body.
Raise the feet slowly while shifting the weight onto the buttocks to maintain balance, using the hands to steady oneself.
When balance is secure, raise the arms so that they are parallel with the floor, wrists about knee level.
If this is too difficult then clasp the hands around the back of the thighs.

Variation 2: This asana is similar to naukasana (boat pose) but the legs and body are raised higher.
Lie down in shavasana.
Breathe slowly and deeply.
While inhaling, tense the muscles and raise the back and legs up so that one is balancing on the buttocks.
Raise the arms so that they are parallel with the floor, wrists at about knee level.

Hold the posture as long as possible without breathing.
Relax back down to shavasana while exhaling.
Breathe normally until breath is steady and heart beat is normal, then repeat at least 7 times.

Benefits: This asana activates the abdominal organs, especially the liver, and strengthens the abdominal muscles. It helps to remove intestinal worms, stimulates intestinal peristalsis and tones the entire visceral region. It tones the spinal nerves, strengthens the spinal muscles and helps to develop the sense of balance and concentration. As an involuntary moolabandha is performed which tightens and strengthens the pelvic floor, it is especially beneficial for girls.

Bumblebee Pose

Stand erect with the feet together.
Relax the whole body and balance the body weight on both feet.
Slowly lean forward, keeping the trunk and head in line.
Simultaneously raise the right leg backwards, keeping the leg straight and in line with the trunk.
The body should rotate about the left hip joint.
Raise the arms behind the back and wriggle the fingers while holding the position.

Remain in that pose as long as possible then relax and repeat the same on the other leg.
When practising with children they can inhale deeply and hum like a bumblebee while exhaling.

Benefits: This is another standing and balancing asana which helps to develop concentration, strengthens the legs, and aids in the attainment of nervous coordination. Some doctors have found that standing and balancing asanas are useful for children suffering from enuresis (bed wetting). This is probably due to improved nervous coordination and strengthening of the lower body.

Stork pose

Stand erect with the feet together and arms at the sides.
Bend the right knee and bring the right foot up behind the back.
Raise the hands to the chest with the palms together, fixing the eyes on a spot on the floor.
Bend the body forward slightly at the hips.
Hold the position as long as possible then relax.
Practise with the left leg up.

Benefits: The stork pose aids in the development of balance and concentration.

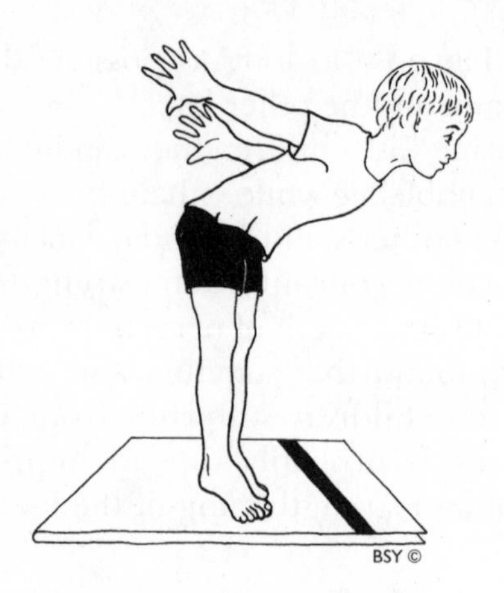

Ostrich pose

Stand erect with the feet only slightly apart.

Bend forward slightly at the hips and raise the arms up behind the back with the fingers spread wide, the head up and facing the front.

Slowly move up onto tiptoes.

This practice can be made dynamic by having the children run around on the toes with the fingers wriggling behind the back.

Benefits: This asana is useful for developing balance, attention and concentration.

As a dynamic pose it is the ostrich running around, releasing tensions. When taught as a static pose, it is a bird standing on a branch, rising up on the tiptoes before he flies off.

Mandukasana (hopping frog pose)

Squat with the legs wide enough apart to have the feet flat on the floor.

Make fists with the hands and cross the wrists, then bring the hands to rest on the top of the head.

Move the weight of the body up onto the toes and hop forward.

Repeat several times.

Benefits: This asana is particularly useful for strengthening the legs and developing balance.

Variation: Hopping rabbit pose

Another variation is to make fists and bring the arms up so that the right hand is placed above the right ear and left hand above the left ear, with the index fingers pointing up like rabbit's ears.

Poorna Bhujangasana (full cobra pose)

Assume bhujangasana.

Holding the position, breathe in and out normally a few times.

Bend the knees and try to touch the back of the head with the toes or the soles of the feet.

Breathe normally in the final pose.

Hold for as long as is comfortable.

Lower the feet and relax.

Benefits: This asana has all the benefits of bhujangasana. It is a very good asana for children and young people, otherwise it is only for adepts with a very supple back.

Vrischikasana (scorpion pose)

Sit in vajrasana and place the forearms and hands down on the floor in front of the knees.

Place the forehead on the floor, between the forearms, against the hands.

Straighten the knees so that you are balanced on the forearms, hands, head and the toes.

Walk up as close to the body as possible.

Then lift the feet off the floor, straight up as in sirshasana (headstand pose).

Slowly bend the knees, bring the feet towards the head and raise the head towards the feet.

Contra-indications: Until this asana is perfected, it should be practised with guidance. Do not practise near furniture or other objects in case of loss of balance.

People with high blood pressure, vertigo, heart problems, cerebral thrombosis or chronic catarrh should not practise this asana. It should be attempted only when all the inverted poses can be performed without the slightest difficulty.

Benefits: This asana reorganizes the vital life force in the body i.e. prana, which is the key to the conquest of physical ageing. It brings about increased nervous stability, and increases the blood flow to the brain and pituitary gland, thereby helping to rectify nervous disorders and glandular malfunctions.

Vrischikasana increases circulation in the lower limbs and abdomen, revitalizing all the bodily systems, alleviating piles and varicose veins, and toning the reproductive organs.

The highly arched position of the back tones the spinal nerves, makes the muscles supple and loosens the vertebrae. It strengthens the arms and develops balance and concentration.

25

Object Asanas

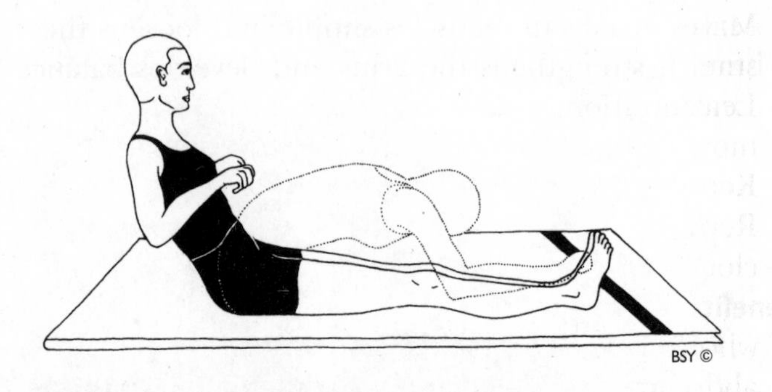

Nauka Sanchalanasana (rowing the boat)

Sit in the base position with legs outstretched in front of the body. Make movements as if rowing a boat.

While inhaling lean back and bring the fists up alongside the body and up over the head in a circular motion.

While exhaling bend the body forward, bringing the arms down with the fists coming near to the feet on either side.

Inhale, let the fists slide up the legs and alongside the body while raising and leaning the body backwards a little.

Exhale and bend forward bringing arms down to feet as before.

Row forwards like this 10 times then reverse the rowing movement 10 times.

Benefits: This pose activates the abdomen and massages all the abdominal organs and muscles. It stretches the hamstring muscles and prepares for paschimottanasana.

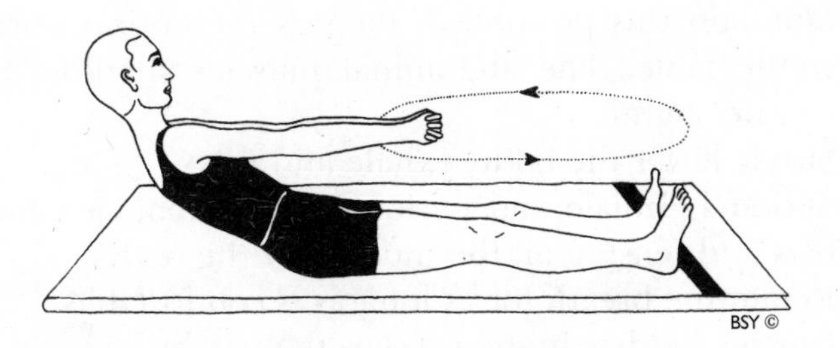

Chakki Chalanasana (churning the mill)

Sit in the base position with the arms stretched out in front of the body, fingers interlocked.

Make horizontal circular movements with the arms, as if stirring a big pot, or grinding corn at a mill.

Lean as far forward and backward as possible, while moving the body in a circular motion from the waist only.

Keep the elbows straight throughout.

Repeat this practice 10 times clockwise and 10 times anti-clockwise.

Benefits: This is a an excellent practice to limber up the whole body. The nerves and organs of the pelvis and abdomen are toned, and regulation of the menstrual cycle is assisted.

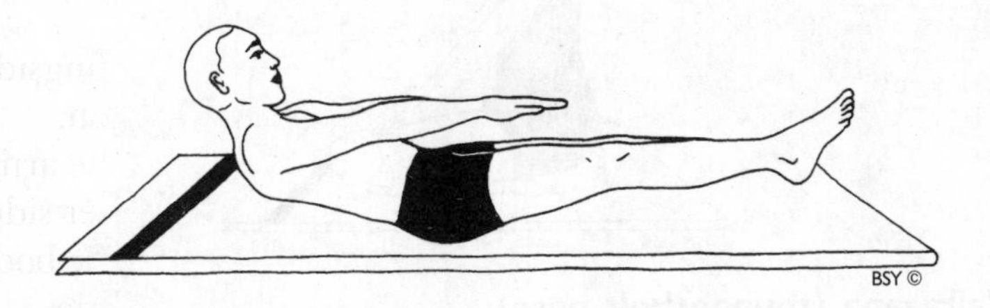

Naukasana (boat pose)

Lie on the back, arms at the sides, with palms down.

Inhale then raise the legs, trunk, arms and head about 15 cm from the floor.

Balance on the buttocks.

The arms are to be held at the same level and in line with the toes. Retain the breath inside.

Maintain this position as long as retention of breath is comfortable. The abdominal muscles should begin to vibrate slightly.
Slowly lower the body, exhale and relax.

Variation 1: Inhale and perform naukasana, clenching the fists and tensing all the muscles of the body.
Retain the breath for as long as is comfortable.
In one sudden motion, relax the whole body, letting it drop on the floor while exhaling.
It is important that the head and feet are no more than 15 cm from the floor in order to avoid banging the head against the floor.

Benefits: This exercise is recommended for stutterers, and also for those plagued by stomach or intestinal worms. It is beneficial for nervous or tense children as it brings about a feeling of immediate relaxation.

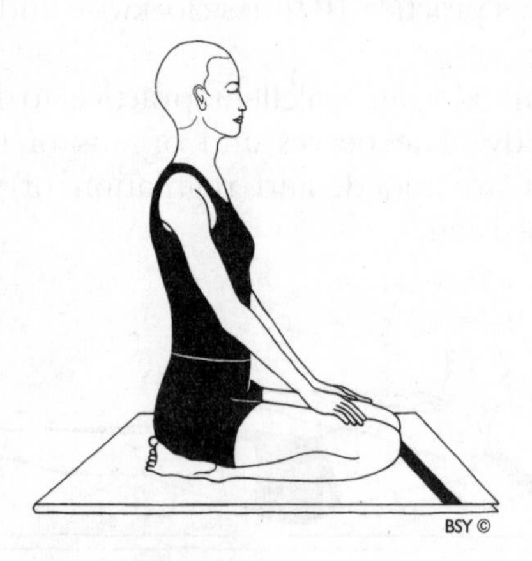

Vajrasana (thunderbolt pose)

Assume a kneeling position.
Bring the big toes together and separate the heels, soles facing upwards.
Sit between the heels while keeping the knees together.
Place the hands on the knees.
Be aware of the breath.
With practise this asana will become very comfortable.

Benefits: By sitting in this posture regularly for ten to fifteen minutes after every meal, one can avoid, relieve and eliminate indigestion and constipation. It relieves peptic ulcers and other stomach ailments. Added nourishment and blood are sent to the nerves and muscles of the thighs, improving circulation.

This pose can be also be used for sitting quietly.

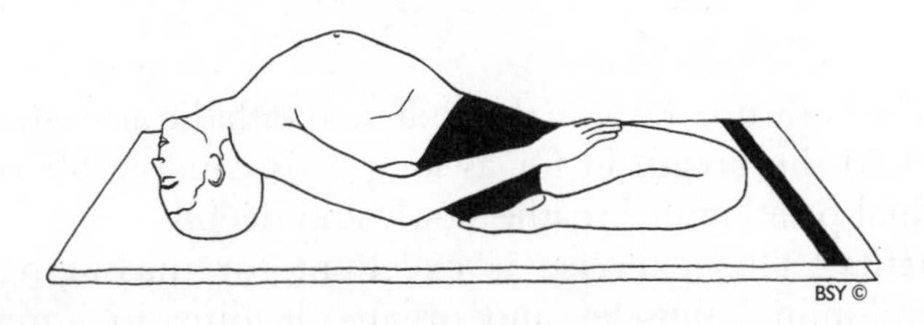

Supta Vajrasana (sleeping thunderbolt pose)

While in vajrasana, slowly bend backwards using the support of the elbows until the top of the head touches the floor, and fully arch the back.

The knees should remain on the floor.

The hands are placed on the thighs.

Close the eyes, relax the body and breathe slowly and deeply.

Benefits: This asana massages the abdominal organs, aiding in the relief and elimination of constipation and digestive ailments. It is beneficial for the relief of asthma, bronchitis and other lung problems. It is also useful in the case of an overactive thyroid gland.

Dhanurasana (bow pose)

Lie on the stomach, legs together, arms beside the body.

Bend the knees and hold the ankles with the hands.

Head, chest and thighs are raised as far as possible so that the body resembles a bow, and the lower legs and arms the bowstring.

Expand the chest and stretch the body by pulling on the ankles while pushing the feet away from the body.

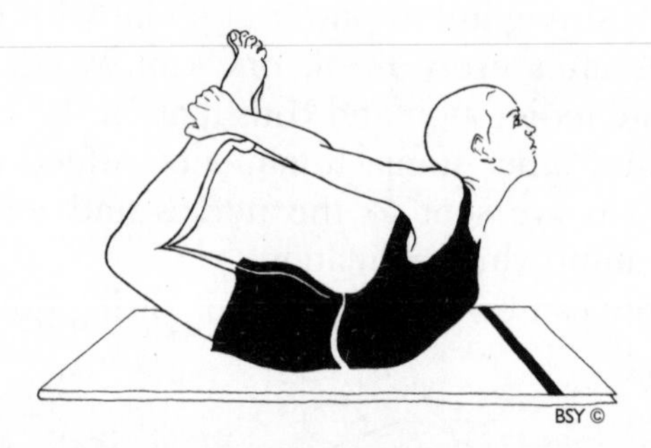

The body now rests on the abdomen with the arms straight. Hold the breath in for as long as is comfortable in the final position or breathe slowly and deeply.

Benefits: This exercise is excellent for massaging the abdominal muscles and organs, leading to improved functioning of the digestive, eliminative and reproductive organs. It is beneficial to those suffering from gastrointestinal diseases, and is effective in cases of chronic constipation and sluggishness of the liver. The spinal cord is kept supple. Chest ailments, including asthma, are relieved.

Chakrasana (wheel pose)

Lie in shavasana.

Bend the knees and bring the heels to touch the buttocks with the feet about 30 cm apart.

Raise the arms and bend the elbows and place the palms of the hands just above the shoulders on the floor.

Let the fingertips point towards the shoulders.

Inhale and then hold the breath in as you slowly raise the trunk, letting the head drop back gently to allow the crown to support the weight of the upper body.

the knees will form right angles.

Then straighten the arms and legs and lift the head off the ground and raise the body to its fully arched height.

Slowly lower the body back to the headbase position, then the supine position while exhaling.

This is one round.
Rest and check the breath rate and heartbeat, allowing them to become normal.
Practise up to 3 rounds.
When the position can be held comfortably one can breathe normally in the final position.

Contra-indications: Chakrasana should not be practised by sufferers of high blood pressure, coronary ailments, stomach ulcers, toxic intestines, partial deafness or dilated eye capillaries.
It should also not be practised by anyone who has recently fractured bones or undergone abdominal operations. It is not to be practised until one has mastered preliminary and intermediate backward bending poses.

Benefits: This asana is beneficial for the entire nervous, digestive, respiratory, cardiovascular and glandular system. It influences all the hormonal secretions and relieves many ailments of the female reproductive system.

Practice note: Children, especially those from about six onwards, love this asana and usually take to it quite quickly. They call it the crab and often walk all round the room while doing this asana dynamically. It can be made more difficult and therefore more like a wheel by bringing the hands and feet closer together in the final pose.

Ardha Chandrasana (crescent moon pose)

Kneel with the legs together and arms by the sides.

Inhale while stepping forward with the left foot.

Bend forward and place the hands by the sides of the left foot, palms flat on the floor.

Stretch the right leg backwards and arch the back and neck, bringing the chin up as high as possible.

Bring the palms of the hands together, slowly bring them up over the head and stretch back, following the arching line of the back and legs on through to the fingertips.

Separate the hands if you find arching the spine too difficult.

Exhale while returning the hands back down by the side, relaxing the arch and bringing the left knee back beside the right one.

Repeat the same sequence with the right leg.

Practise to each side at least 5 times.

Benefits: This asana limbers and strengthens the entire skeletal structure. It is especially beneficial for female disorders related to the ovaries, uterus and urinary tract. It gives a good stretch to the chest and neck, relieving respiratory ailments, as well as sore throat, tonsilitis, cough and cold. It also develops balance and concentration.

Practice note: An easier version of this asana can be done without stretching the arms over the head.

Setu Asana (bridge pose)

Sit in the base position, with the legs stretched out in front of the body, palms on the floor about 30 cm behind the buttocks with the fingertips pointing back.

Lift the buttocks and bring the soles of the feet down flat on the floor.

Let the arms and hands, together with the feet, support the body weight. Let the head hang down, chin in line with the chest.

Hold as long as possible.

Lower the buttocks back down to the floor as the toes are raised off the floor and feet rest again on the heels.

Repeat up to 3 times.

Benefits: This asana tones the lumbar region of the spine and the Achilles tendons at the rear of the ankles.

Setu Baddhasana (bound bridge pose)

Variation 1: This is the easy method to be used with young children.

Lie in shavasana. Bend the knees and bring the heels as close to the buttocks as possible.

Arch the back and lift the stomach up while bringing the hips off the floor.

Bend the elbows and place the hands at the waist, thumbs towards stomach and fingertips towards the spine.

Hold the position as long as is comfortable.

Lower the buttocks to the floor and relax the back down to the floor.

Repeat several times.

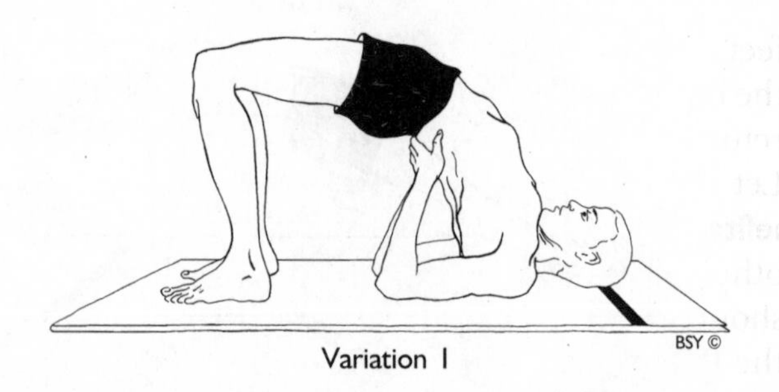

Variation 1

Variation 2: This method is only to be taught to those who have reached puberty.

From shavasana, the legs are brought up into sarvangasana, the shoulderstand pose.

Bend the elbows and place the hands at the waist, thumbs towards the stomach and fingertips towards the spine. This is very important as you will see later.

The right knee is bent and the sole of the right foot is brought to rest just above the left knee. Then bend the left knee so that the foot is approaching the floor.

Bend at the waist, let the left foot come to rest on the floor, then bring the right foot down to the floor beside the left.

Slide the feet away from the body and balance on the back of the head, shoulders, upper arms, elbows and soles of the feet for as long as possible.

Then walk the feet back as close to the body as possible.

Bring the sole of the right foot to rest above the left knee once again. Move up on to the tips of the left toes and using the muscles of the back, lift up, bringing the left toes off the floor and straighten the right knee and place the right leg alongside the left, stretched overhead in sarvangasana. Return to shavasana if necessary.

Otherwise repeat the same sequence but put the left foot above the right knee and lower the right foot to the floor, returning on the right foot etc.

Return to shavasana again if necessary, or from sarvangasana separate the feet slightly, about 15 cm.

Bend both knees and the waist while slowly lowering both

feet over the head to the floor. Stretch the feet away from the body, hold the posture as long as possible in halasana, return to sarvangasana then shavasana.

Let the breath and heartbeat return to normal.

Benefits: This asana stretches and massages the colon and other abdominal organs. It is beneficial for rounded shoulders and backache. It is especially useful for toning the female reproductive organs. It is a good preparatory pose for chakrasana. The spinal arch is given a good backward bend and it is, therefore, a good posture to use as a counterpose for forward bending asanas like halasana, paschimottanasana etc.

Practice note: Care should be taken not to strain.

Dolasana (pendulum pose)

Stand upright with the feet about a metre apart.

Raise the arms and interlock the fingers behind the neck with the elbows pointing sideways.

Inhale and turn slightly to the right with the upper part of the body.

Exhaling, bend forward bringing the head to the right knee.

Holding the breath outside, swing the head and upper trunk from the right knee to the left knee and back.

Repeat 3 times.

Slowly return to the upright position while inhaling, and centre the body.

Repeat the process, but this time bend the trunk to the left knee from the upright position. Keep the legs straight throughout the whole asana.

Repeat at least 5 times to each side.

Benefits: This is an excellent asana for strengthening the arms, shoulders and back. It makes the waistline slim and strong and tones the spinal nerves. It strengthens the lungs and develops balance and concentration.

Pada Hastasana (forward bending or pincer pose)

Stand with the spine erect and hands beside the body.

While exhaling slowly bend forward, first the upper trunk and eventually the lower trunk.

The body should bend forward at the hips as though there are no muscles in the back.

Place the fingers underneath the toes or touch the palms on the ground. If this is not possible, then bring the tips of the fingers as near to the floor as possible.

Try to bring the forehead to the knees.

While inhaling come back to the starting position.

To practise the static form maintain this pose as long as is comfortable, then slowly return to the starting position.

Keep the legs straight all throughout the movement but do not strain the hamstring muscles at the back of the legs or the back muscles by forcing the body to bend too far forwards.

Benefits: This asana should not be practised by anyone suffering from serious back ailments, sciatica, heart disease high blood pressure or hernia. Pada hastasana removes excess fat, particularly if done dynamically. It eliminates flatulence, constipation and indigestion. It makes the spinal column and back muscles loose and supple. All the spinal nerves are stimulated and toned, and the body's metabolism is speeded up. It influences the sexual and eliminative organs, removing many sexual ailments. It improves the elimination of waste matter from the body and so reduces the likelihood of the occurrence of disease. This asana directs a good flow of blood to the brain and facial organs. This is a very useful asana and can be practised at any time of the day, though not after meals. It is a standing version of the forward bending practice of paschimottanasana.

Practice note: In the dynamic form, raise the arms above the head in the standing position, bend forward and touch the hands to the floor.

Remain for 1 or 2 seconds then return to the upright position.

Sumeru Asana (summit pose)

Sit in vajrasana then move into the cat pose with the toes on the floor, heels pointing upwards.

Exhaling bring the soles of the feet down to the floor, placing the heels on the floor if possible, while raising the buttocks and straightening the knees.

The back and arms should form a straight line with the head between the elbows.

The body should be in the form of a triangle.

Raise the heels, bend the knees and return to the cat pose while inhaling.

Try to maintain the final pose for at least 30 seconds.
Practise up to 10 times.

Benefits: This asana should not be practised by sufferers of vertigo or high blood pressure. It stretches the Achilles tendons, hamstrings and calf muscles, strengthens the muscles in the arms and legs, and tones the spinal nerves. This is a good substitute asana for sirshasana for sufferers of myopia.

Hasta Pada Angushthasana (finger to toe stretch or fan pose)

Lie on the right side with arms stretched over and behind the head.
The left foot should rest on the right foot and the left palm on the right palm.
While inhaling deeply, slowly raise the left leg and arm without bending either, so that they each form a 45 degree angle with the floor.
Then raise them to their full extent, and hold the toes without bending the knee.
This is the final position.
The fan is fully opened.
While exhaling slowly bring the leg and arm back to the starting position.
Practise up to 5 times.
Turn over and repeat the movement with the right leg and arm.

Benefits: This asana makes the hip joints flexible and is useful for reducing fat on the hips and thighs. It is especially beneficial for young girls as it helps the proper development and shaping of the pelvis.

Dynamic Paschimottanasana (back stretch or hairpin pose)

Lie down flat on the back.
Extend the arms overhead onto the floor and inhale.
Come to a sitting position and exhale.
While retaining the breath outside, bend forward and hold the toes, touching the forehead to the knees.
In a single movement, return to a lying position and inhale.

Benefits: This is an effective asana against flatulence and for the removal of excess fat. The spinal column is made more supple. The circulation and metabolic processes are speeded up.

This asana is especially recommended for those suffering from diabetes.

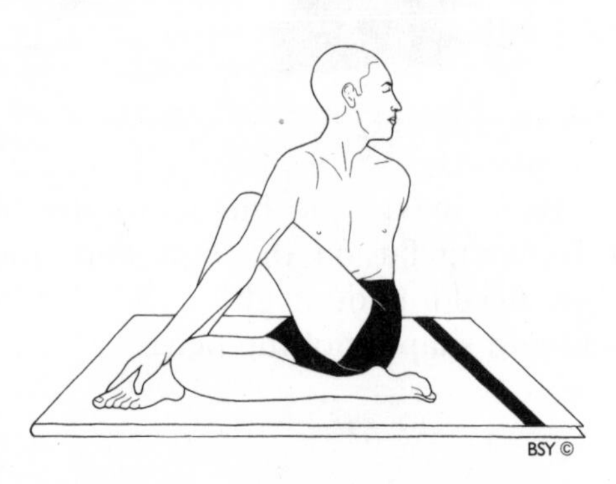

Ardha Matsyendrasana (half spinal twist)

Sit with the legs stretched out in front of the body.

Place the left foot on the floor on the outside of the right knee.

The toes of the left foot should face forward.

Bend the right leg and place the right heel against the left buttock.

Now bring the right shoulder against the outside of the left knee.

Press the knee towards the right and place the right arm to the outside of the left leg and hold the left foot with the right hand.

Slowly turn the body to the left side, placing the left arm around the back and look over the left shoulder.

The head and the spinal cord should be twisted to the maximum.

Do not strain the back.

Breathe deeply without strain for 5 breaths.

Reverse the movements to come out of the posture, then change legs and repeat to the opposite side.

Benefits: This asana simultaneously stretches the muscles on one side of the back and abdomen while contracting the muscles on the other side. The lateral movements of the spine are developed and the spinal nerves are toned. The abdominal organs receive a natural massage and the secretion of adrenaline and bile is regulated. The pancreas is well stimulated.

Tadasana (palm tree pose)

Stand erect, interlock the fingers and place the hands, palms up, on top of the head. Inhale and stretch the arms above the head, rising up onto the tiptoes. Stretch the whole body from top to bottom, without losing your balance.

Exhale and lower the heels and arms to the starting position.

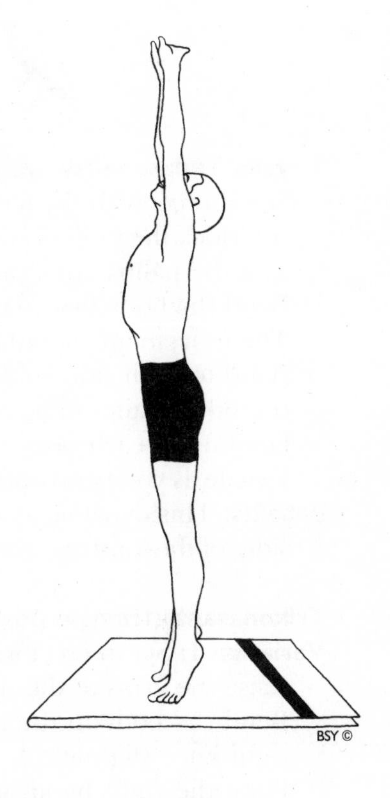

Benefits: As tadasana stretches the rectus abdomini, it opens the cardiac and pyloric sphincters of the digestive system, relieving gastric problems such as gas and constipation. It also helps children to straighten their spines, aids in correcting the posture and is excellent for young growing bodies.

Tiryaka Tadasana (swaying palm tree pose)

Stand erect with the feet about 60 cm apart.

Interlock the fingers and stretch the arms above the head with the palms up towards the ceiling.

Bend the body first to the right and then to the left.

The movement should come from the waist.

Bend to each side 10 times then relax the arms down to the sides. Can also be practised by rising on the toes and bending to each side.

Exhale as you bend and inhale as you come to the centre.

Benefits: This dynamic asana is very good for digestion. The sides of the waist are exercised. It helps to develop balance.

Trikonasana (triangle pose)

Variation 1: Stand erect with the feet about a metre apart.

Raise the arms to the side to form one straight line.

Bend the body to the right, simultaneously bending the right knee slightly.

Place the right hand on the right foot, keeping the two arms in line with each other. Look up at the left hand.

Return to the standing position with the arms still in one straight line.

Repeat to the opposite side, bending the left knee slightly.

Practise 5 rounds.

Variation 2

Variation 1

Variation 2: Repeat the basic form, but instead of keeping the upper arm vertical in the final position, lower it over the ear until it is parallel to the floor.

Variation 3: Stand with the feet wide apart.

Place the left palm on the side of the waist, fingers pointing down. Bend slowly to the right side while sliding the right hand down the right leg to the foot.

If you cannot touch the foot do not strain.

Raise the body to the vertical position, sliding the right hand slowly up the leg to the waist.

Repeat to the other side.

Breathe slowly in to centre, out to the side.

Practise 5 rounds.

Variation 4: Stand with the feet a shoulder's width apart.

While breathing in, raise the arms to each side until horizontal.

This is the starting position.

Variation 3

BSY ©

Variation 4

BSY ©

While breathing out, bend forward, then twist the trunk and arms so that the right hand touches the left foot.
The left arm should point up vertically.
The face should be directed towards the ceiling with the eyes gazing at the raised left hand.
Hold the breath in the final pose for 3 seconds, feeling the twist and stretch of the back.
Then raise the body to the starting position while breathing in, keeping the arms outstretched to the sides.
Breathe out while twisting to the right side, so that the left hand touches the right foot. Look up and gaze at the right hand.
Hold this final pose while retaining the breath for 3 seconds.
Then breathe in and return to the starting position.
Do not lower the arms.
This is one round. Practise 5 rounds.

Benefits: This series affects the muscles on the sides of the trunk, waist and backs of the legs. It stimulates the nervous system and alleviates nervous depression. It keeps the spine supple and massages the abdominal organs. Appetite and digestion are improved, and constipation relieved.

Sarvangasana (shoulder stand or candle pose)

Lie down flat on the back, palms down beside the thighs. Raise the legs with bent knees and slowly roll the back up to the shoulders until the chin touches the chest. Use the hands as a support, resting on the elbows.

Straighten the legs vertically.

The body should now be at a right angle to the head, neck, shoulders and elbows.

The back should be straight, the chin pressing the chest.

To return to the lying position, firstly bring the knees down to the forehead, place the hands on the floor, and lower the body and legs slowly to the floor.

BSY ©

Hold the breath in while raising and lowering the body.

Benefits: Daily practice of sarvangasana supplies the thyroid gland with a rich flow of blood, thus stimulating this gland which is responsible for respiratory exchange, genital and sexual development, and the growth of the bones. So young children whose bodies have not developed normally should practise this asana. Children with normal growth should only practise this asana in a dynamic form, as one of many postures, in order that natural development may continue on its own. After puberty this asana may be practised without harm and with great benefit.

Halasana (plough or wheelbarrow pose)

Lie flat on the back with the hands palms down beside the thighs.

Raise both legs and guide them over the head until the toes touch the floor.

The legs should remain straight.

Support the back with the hands if necessary.

Benefits: This posture is recommended for diabetics. It aids the rejuvenation of the pancreas as well as the regulation of adrenaline in the system. Daily practice is beneficial to girls who are established in maturity and also to people who wish to lose weight. If used with very young children it should be done as a dynamic asana, not held for any length of time (as in the blossoming lotus flower for preschool children).

Teapot Pose

Balance on the left leg holding the right foot with the right hand.

The left elbow is bent and resting against the body. The left wrist is bent with the hand sticking out, fingers pointing away from the body at about shoulder height.

Look straight ahead at a fixed point.

When balance has been achieved then slowly bend forward at the hips, pushing the right foot against the hand, causing it to come up behind the back, maintaining balance all the time.

Simultaneously reach forward a little with the left arm.

Hold for as long as is comfortable.

Straighten the body while bringing the right foot back down to the floor. Relax.

Practise bringing up the left foot and standing on the right leg.

BSY ©

Benefits: This exercise is used frequently with very young children and is a very good way to introduce them to balancing asanas.

It develops strength in the legs and helps develop concentration and attention.

Jack Knife Pose

Stand with feet together and body straight, arms hanging relaxed beside the body.

While exhaling, slowly bend the torso forward bringing the head towards the knees.

Keeping the elbows straight, bring the arms back parallel with the floor at about knee level.

Tuck the chin in closely so the jack knife is neatly closed.

Benefits: This asana is beneficial in the elimination and prevention of stomach and abdominal ailments. Any surplus fat in the abdominal region is reduced. Digestion and blood circulation are improved.

BSY ©

This posture makes the spine supple and tones the spinal nerves and muscles. It requires balance so it is very good for developing both balance and concentration.

Akarna Dhanurasana (bow and arrow pose)

Stand erect with the feet about a shoulder width apart and the arms at the sides.

Take a short step forward with the left leg.

Clench the left fist and stretch it up and sideways so that it is over the left foot and slightly above eye level.

Clench the right fist and then bring it slightly behind the left fist.

Feel as though you are holding a bow.

While inhaling deeply, gaze over your left fist and pull your right fist back to the right ear, as if drawing a bow.

The head should travel slightly backwards with this motion so that the neck muscles become taut.

Exhale while releasing the imaginary bow string.

Then relax the neck and bring the right fist forward to the left fist. Relax the arms to the sides and step back with the left foot so that it is in line with the right.

Practise 5 times on each side.

Benefits: This asana develops the biceps, pectoral and neck muscles, so it is an excellent practice for young, developing bodies.

Eka Pada Pranamasana (one legged prayer or tree pose)

Stand erect with the feet together and arms at the sides.

Raise one foot and place the sole against the inside of the opposite upper thigh.

The heel should touch the perineum and the knee point out to the side.

Raise the hands and place the palms together in front of the chest.

Fix the eyes on a point straight ahead.

Hold for as long as possible. Then change sides.

Practise up to 3 rounds on each leg.

Benefits: This asana develops equilibrium, balance and concentration. It strengthens the muscles of the legs, ankles and feet.

Variation: Assume the final position. Keep the gaze focused at eye level, inhale and raise the arms above the head, palms together. Hold the position with the breath inside and, on exhalation, lower the hands back in front of the chest. Repeat on the other side.

Padmasana (lotus pose)

Sit with the legs outstretched.

Slowly and carefully bend one leg and place the foot on top of the opposite thigh.

The sole should face upward and the heel should be close to the pubic bone.

When this feels comfortable, bend the other leg and place the foot on top of the opposite thigh.

Both knees should, ideally, touch the ground in the final position.

The head and spine should be held upright and the shoulders relaxed.

Place the hands on the knees.

Close the eyes and try to sit quietly without moving the body for one or two minutes, breathing very slowly.

Contra-indications: Those who suffer from sciatica, sacral infections or weak or injured knees should not perform this asana. This asana should not be attempted until flexibility of the knees has been developed.

Benefits: This asana allows the body to be held completely steady. As the body is steadied the mind becomes calm. Padmasana tones up the coccygeal and sacral nerves since the normally large blood flow into the legs is largely redirected to the abdominal region. The digestive process is also stimulated.

Lolasana (swinging pose)

Sit in padmasana.

Place the palms on the floor next to the thighs.

Inhale, then raise the body from the floor and balance on the hands.

Swing the body backwards and forwards between the arms for as long as possible.

Then come back to the sitting position and exhale.

Rest in the sitting position.

Repeat the pose with the legs crossed the other way.

Benefits: This pose is especially good for children. Arms, wrists and shoulders are strengthened and trembling hands are rectified. It generates control, coordination and dexterity. The abdominal muscles are exercised. Balance is also developed.

Baddha Padmasana (locked lotus pose)

Sit in padmasana.

Take the arms behind the back and cross them.

Leaning forward slightly, and reach for the right big toe with the right hand and the left big toe with the left hand.

Hold for as long as is comfortable.

Breathe slowly and deeply.

Release the position, then cross the legs the other way around and repeat the practice.

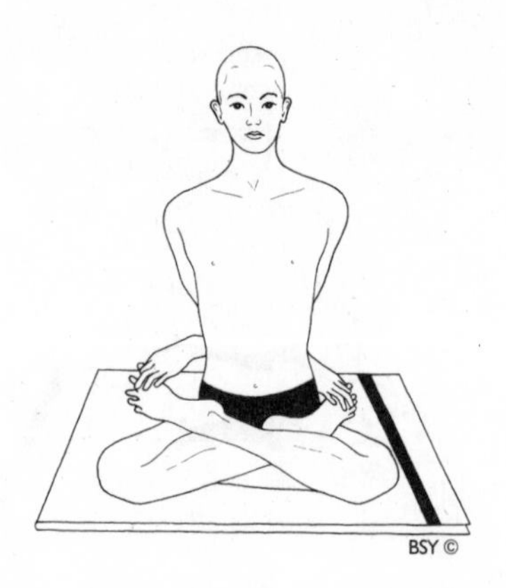

Benefits: Children with poorly developed chests should perform this asana as it encourages normal growth. Shoulder, back and arm pain can also be alleviated.

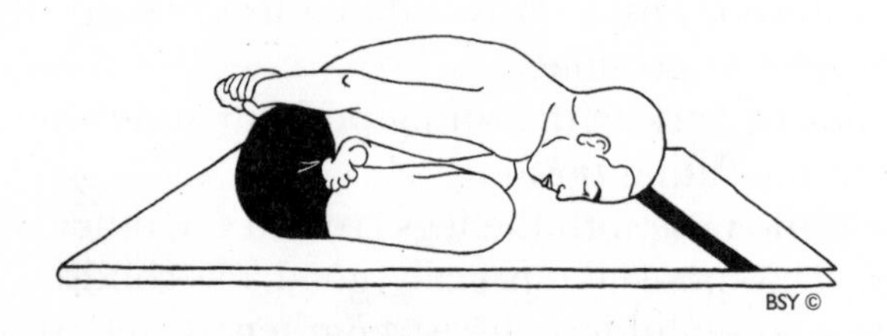

Yogamudrasana (psychic union pose)

Sit in padmasana with both knees touching the floor.
Hold one wrist with the opposite hand behind the back.
Close the eyes.
Inhale, then exhale while slowly bending forward until the forehead touches the floor.
Retain the breath outside for a while, but without any discomfort.
Slowly return to the sitting position while inhaling.

Benefits: This exercise gives energy. It is excellent for massaging the abdominal organs and removing many abdominal ailments, including constipation and indigestion.

26

Characters and Persons

Natavarasana (Lord Krishna's pose)

Stand erect and place the right foot to the left of the left calf with the toes a little above the ground.

The sole of the foot should be almost vertical.

Rest the right calf against the left shin.

Then raise both arms and place the hands as if playing a flute.

Hold the posture for as long as possible and then bring the right foot and hands back to the starting position.

Relax, and then do the same with the left foot while balancing on the right leg.

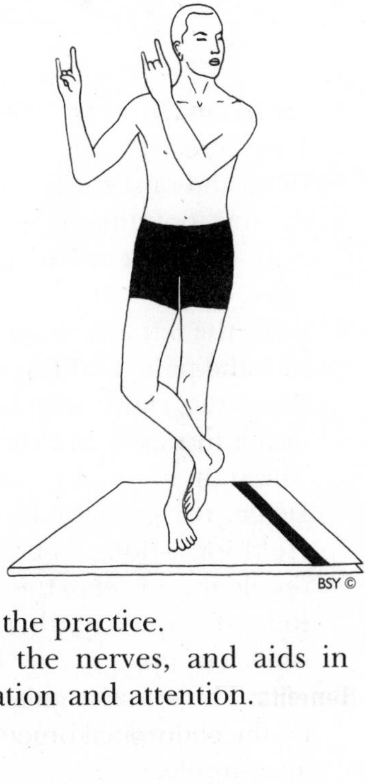

BSY ©

Breathe normally throughout the practice.

Benefits: Natavarasana controls the nerves, and aids in developing balance, concentration and attention.

Natarajasana I (Lord Shiva's dance)

Stand erect.

Bend and raise the left knee so that the thigh is horizontal, the foot pointing away from the body and slightly to the right of the right leg. The right leg is bent slightly at the knee.

Place the left arm across the body in line with the left leg with the palm and fingers facing down.

Bend the right arm at the elbow with the right palm facing forwards and the forearm vertical.

The right elbow is just behind the left wrist.

Do chin or gyana mudra with the fingers.

Hold for as long as possible, then return the left foot to the floor and relax the arms.

Relax completely, then do the same practice with the right foot up.

Benefits: This asana balances the nervous system, aids in bodily control and mental concentration, and makes the legs supple.

Preparatory form

Full form

Natarajasana 2 (Lord Shiva's pose) – preparatory form

Stand erect.

Bend the right knee and grasp the right ankle with the right hand. Slowly raise the right foot behind the back, as high as possible, while reaching upwards and forwards with the left arm.

Bring the tip of the index finger and thumb of the left hand together to form chin mudra, then gaze at the left hand. Hold for as long as possible then bring the right foot back down to the floor while bringing the arms back to the sides.

Relax, then repeat with the left leg.

Natarajasana 2 (Lord Shiva's pose) – full form

This form is similar to the preparatory form except that the right big toe is held instead of the ankle.

The right elbow, which is behind the back, is bent and is pointing upwards.

This position of the hand and arm allows the foot to be brought nearer to the back of the head.
Advanced practitioners with flexible bodies may be able to touch the back of the head with the toes or hold the toes with the hands.

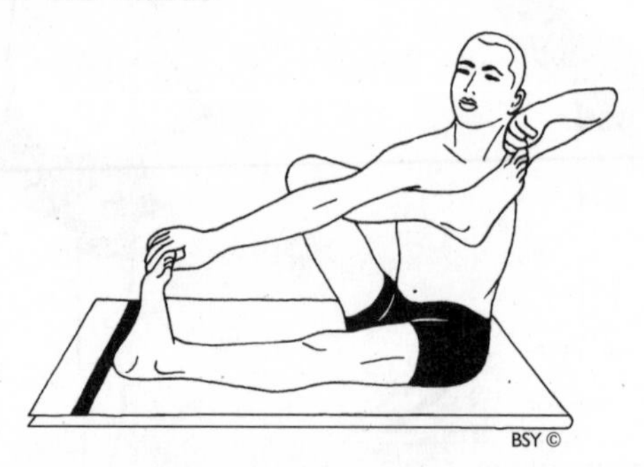

Dhanurakarshanasana (archer's pose)

Sit with the legs stretched forward.
Place the right foot on the left thigh, and grasp the right big toe from the top with the left hand.
Hold the left big toe with the right hand, keeping the leg straight. Inhale, then raise the right big toe to the left ear. Do not bend the neck or back.
Exhale after returning the right foot to the thigh.
This action resembles that of drawing a bow.

Benefits: Tones the abdominal organs, stretches the spine, strengthens the biceps and ankles, and loosens the hip joints and leg muscles.

Arjunasana (balanced archer's pose)

Stand erect with arms hanging relaxed at the sides.
Raise the chin slightly and find a spot on the ceiling a little in front, to gaze at.
Step forward with the right foot, about one foot in front, then bend the right knee.
Slowly raise the left leg bringing the knee back and the sole of the foot turned away from the body as if resting on a wall behind you, or on a chariot.

The head is kept up and facing forward.

When balanced, slowly bring the arms up in front of the body at about shoulder level.

Make a fist with the left hand and bring it along the right arm to ear level.

The right arm is extended in front as if holding a bow, but the fingers are stretched out and the thumb tucked in as if an arrow has been inserted and the bowstring is tautly drawn.

Hold as long as comfortable, while gazing forward.

Bring the arms to the sides and the left foot back down to the floor.

Relax, then repeat with the other leg.

Benefits: This asana develops the brain centre, the cerebellum, which controls fine movements of the body and thereby the ability to move different parts of the body more gracefully and in harmony with each other. It develops balance so concentration is also enhanced, which can be carried over to other fields of activity.

Note: *One often sees pictures of Arjuna and Krishna riding on a chariot. Krishna is driving the chariot for Arjuna the warrior. Arjuna is often depicted standing on one leg, supporting and bracing himself with the other leg against the chariot and having his bow and arrow drawn and ready for shooting.*

Garbha Pindasana (foetus in the womb pose)

Sit in padmasana.

Insert the arms between the thighs and calves just past the elbows.

Bend the elbows and catch hold of the ears and then balance the body on the buttocks.

Retain the balanced pose as long as possible with normal breathing. Then slowly lower the legs, release the arms and relax.

Benefits: This exercise alleviates nervous disorders and also helps to calm an excited, angry mind. In case of habitual and uncontrollable anger, one may practise this asana several times a day. The digestive fire is stimulated and the appetite increased. A fine sense of balance is achieved.

27

Alphabet Asanas

Bhumi Pada Mastakasana (half headstand or letter A pose)

Sit in vajrasana, then assume the cat pose but keep the legs together. Place the crown of the head on the ground between the hands.

Straighten the knees, raise the buttocks and bring the heels down to the floor, if possible, so that one is balancing on the head and feet.

Raise the arms and take hold of the knees with the hands.

Hold the position for as long as possible.

Lower the hands back down to the floor, bend the knees and come back into the cat pose, then sit down on the heels in vajrasana.

The breathing should be normal throughout the practice.

You can follow with tadasana, the counterpose to this asana.

Contra-indications: People with high blood pressure, heart conditions or severe myopia should not practise this asana.

Benefits: This asana is beneficial in cases of low blood pressure. It aids in the attainment of nervous balance, strengthens the head and neck muscles and supplies blood to the brain. It is a good preliminary pose for sirshasana, the headstand pose.

Practice note: Make sure there is sufficient soft padding beneath the head.

Ardha Padma Padmottanasana (half lotus leg stretch or letter L pose)

Sit in the base position with legs stretched forward.

Bend the left knee and place the left foot on top of the right thigh, half lotus style.

Bend the right knee and place the foot flat on the ground.

Raise the right leg and clasp the hands under the thigh.

Fix the gaze on a visible point in front of the body.

Slowly straighten the right leg and balance on the back of the buttocks.

Keep the arms close to the body while still clasping the leg.

Hold for as long as possible.

Then bend the right knee again bringing the foot to the floor.

Stretch the legs in front and relax.

Repeat the process with the right foot on the left thigh.
Practise up to 5 times with each leg.

Benefits: This asana prepares the legs for padmasana (the lotus pose) and aids in the attainment of nervous balance and concentration.

Eka Padasana (one foot or letter T pose)

Stand erect with the feet together.
Raise the arms directly above the head and interlock the fingers.
Slowly lean forward, keeping the trunk and head in line with the straight arms.
Simultaneously raise the left leg backwards, keeping the leg straight and in line with the trunk.
The final pose is attained when the left leg, the trunk, the head and arms lie in one straight, horizontal line.
The right leg should be straight and vertical.
Focus the gaze on the hands.
Remain in the final pose for as long as possible and then slowly return to the starting position.
Repeat the movement raising the right leg backwards.

Benefits: This asana strengthens the arms, wrists and leg muscles. It relaxes the lower back and aids in attainment of nervous co-ordination.

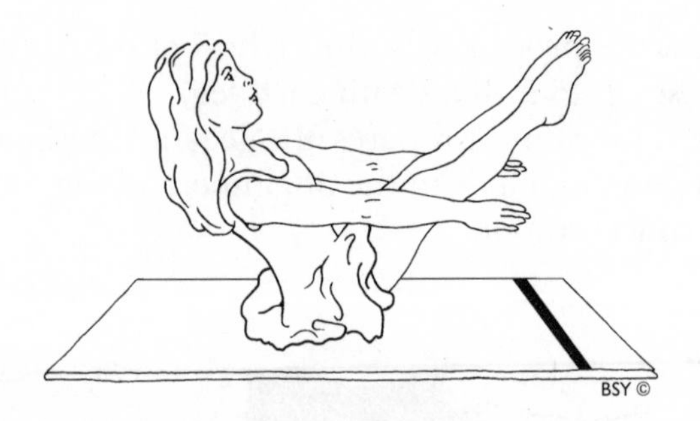

Vajroli Mudra Asana (thunderbolt attitude or letter V pose)

Sit in the base position with the legs stretched out in front of the body but with the palms flat on the floor beside the buttocks, fingers pointing towards the front of the body.

Slowly lift the legs and shift the weight further back onto the buttocks, leaning the torso and head slightly back.

One is balancing on the buttocks.

The head should remain in line with the torso.

Hold as long as possible then bring the legs slowly down to the floor and relax.

When balance is achieved the arms can be raised parallel to the floor.

Benefits: This asana should not be practised by anyone suffering from slipped disc. It activates the abdominal organs and strengthens the abdominal muscles. Balance and concentration are developed.

28

Asanas Done in Pairs

Wheelbarrow

One child is asked to assume bhujangasana, the cobra pose.
The second child lifts one foot and then the other foot of the first child (in bhujangasana), so that he is balancing on the arms.
The second child then slowly walks forward.
At the same time the child in bhujangasana walks forward on his hands.
Do this for a few minutes then stop and relax.
The partners can then change position.

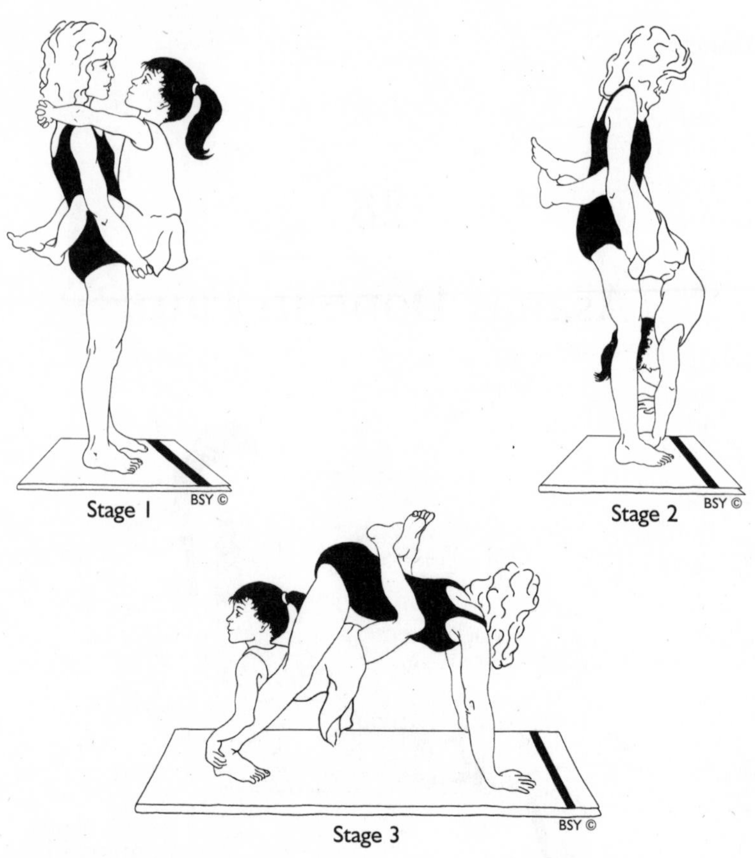

Chinese Dragon

Stage 1: Let the smaller child jump up and lock her legs around the waist of her partner by crossing her ankles.

Stage 2: Then, taking the support of her partner, she should lean backwards, hanging upside down and bring her hands to the ankles of her partner.

Stage 3: The partner should now bend forward bringing her hands to the floor. Then she can walk slowly on her hands and feet with her head raised high.

The smaller child should also raise her head high.

To release the position the smaller child should first lower one leg slowly to the floor, followed by the other. Her partner should then walk forward out of the pose.

Dancing Duo

This is similar to Natarajasana, preparatory form, except that the children hold hands with the outstretched arm.

During the practice, one child uses the left leg first and the other uses the right leg first, and so on.

Both children help each other to balance.

Double Windmill

Both children should stand back to back with their arms against each other.

One child slowly raises his left arm forwards and up and around and down behind him.

The second child, therefore, raises his right arm back and up and over and down in front of him.

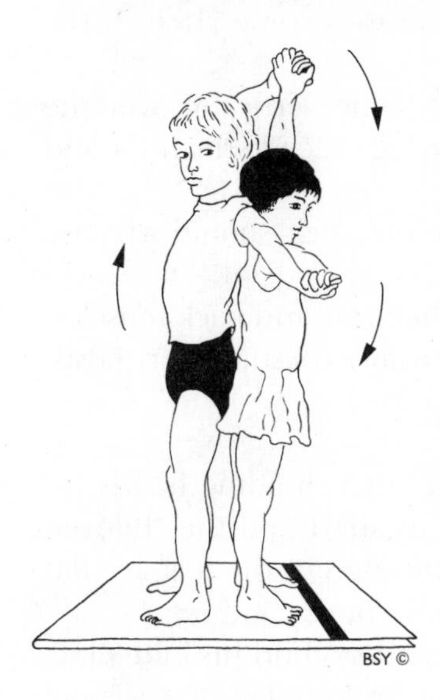

This is repeated at least five times.

Then the same practice is done with the right arm of the first child and the left arm of the second child.

Then both arms are practised alternately.

Then change and let the second child bring the arms up, forward, over and down in front and so on.

The children may find it easier to hold hands.

Stambhan Asana (posture of retention)

Both children should lie down on their backs with the crowns of their heads in contact.

They should stretch both arms sideways and hold each other's hands at arm's length.

The arms must be tensed and the heads must press against each other.

One child should raise his legs to a vertical position, then slowly lower the feet so that the toes come close to the partner's navel.

Then raise the legs again, this time vertically over the partner's head. Slowly lower the legs back to the floor and relax.

The children should alternate and each should practise up to 5 times.

Benefits: This asana strengthens the arms and back muscles, providing stimulation which activates intestinal peristalsis.

See-sawing

Both children should face each other, holding hands.

The feet are placed about 30 cm apart and the children then squat, making sure that the soles of the feet are flat on the ground, not on the toes.

Still holding hands, one child sits down on his buttocks.

Then as the second child sits on his buttocks he pulls the first child back up into the squatting position.

The first child again sits down, pulling the second child back up into the squatting position.
In this way they can continue see-sawing.

Benefits: This practice helps the children to develop balance while strengthening and improving the circulation in the legs and making the knees flexible.

29

Pranayama

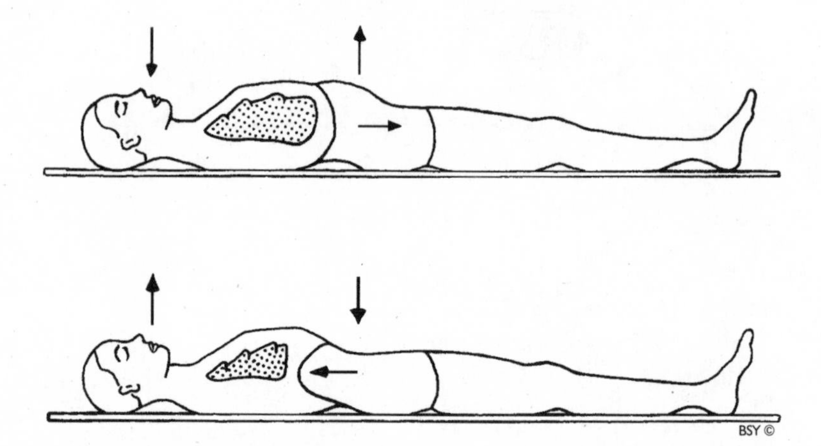

Abdominal Breathing

To encourage abdominal breathing, ask the child to lie down on the floor.

Place a small paper boat, which the child has made previously, at the navel.

Explain that when he breathes in, a wave is created by the stomach as it swells out.

When he breathes out the wave subsides.

By being able to watch the boat on the waves, the child is able to develop awareness of the abdomen and abdominal breathing which the young child does unconsciously.

Benefits: Abdominal breathing is really a natural breath for children. It is only as we become adults that we start to breathe incorrectly. Abdominal breathing has been shown to be the best form of breathing because it requires less energy than chest or upper lung breathing, and the oxygen/carbon dioxide exchange is greater during this type of breathing.

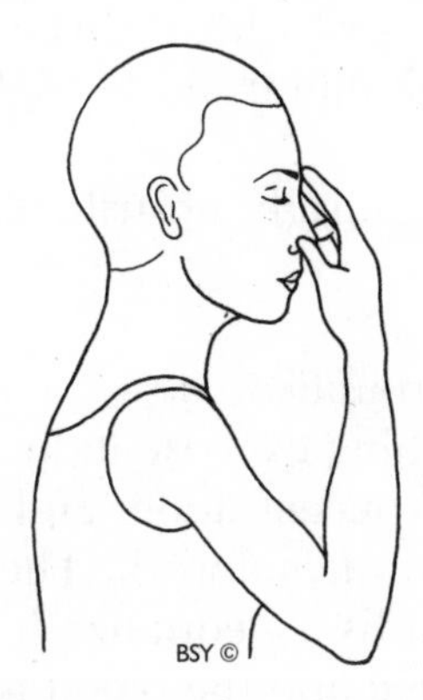

Nadi Shodhana Pranayama (alternate nostril breathing)

Sit in any comfortable asana.

Ensure that the spine is erect and both knees are resting on the floor.

Relax the whole body and close the eyes.

The left hand is placed on the left knee.

The right hand is used to close the nostrils.

The index and middle fingers are placed in the centre of the eyebrows and remain in this position throughout the practice.

The thumb is used to close the right nostril and the ring finger is used to close the left nostril.

Stage 1: Preparatory practice

Close the right nostril with the thumb.

Inhale and exhale through the left nostril 5 times, keeping the right nostril closed throughout.

Then close the left nostril with the ring finger and open the right nostril.

Inhale and exhale through the right nostril 5 times.
The process of inhaling and exhaling 5 times through each nostril is equal to one round.
Practise 5 to 10 rounds.

Stage 2: Happy breathing

Close the right nostril with the thumb.
Inhale through the left nostril.
Close the left nostril with the ring finger. Release the pressure of the thumb from the right nostril and exhale through the right.
Inhale through the right nostril and exhale through the left nostril.
This is one round.
Practise 5 to 10 rounds.

Benefits: This breathing exercise induces tranquillity, clarity of thought and concentration, and is recommended for those engaged in mental work. The flow of prana in ida and pingala nadis is equalized. Carbon dioxide is efficiently expelled and the blood is purified of toxins.

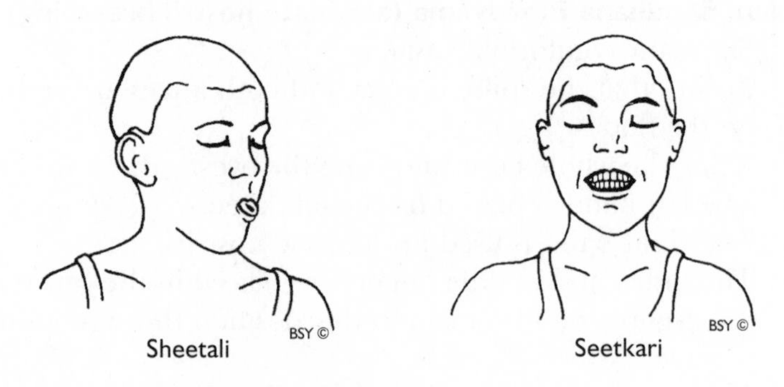

Sheetali Seetkari

Sheetali Pranayama (cooling breath)

Sit in any comfortable asana with the spine erect and both knees resting on the floor. Place the hands on the knees.
Extend the tongue outside the mouth as far as possible.
Roll the sides of the tongue into a tube.
Inhale through the funnelled tongue as though trying to swallow air into the stomach.

Release the tongue, close the mouth and exhale through the nose.

Practise 10 rounds.

Benefits: This practice purifies the blood and prevents and relieves high blood pressure. It induces mental, psychic and muscular calmness, and also eliminates the feeling of thirst.

Seetkari Pranayama (hissing breath)

Sit in any comfortable asana with the spine erect and both knees resting on the floor. Place the hands on the knees.

Fold the tongue back and place it against the palate.

Hold the teeth lightly together and separate the lips.

Inhale slowly and deeply through the teeth.

Close the lips and exhale slowly through the nose.

Practise 10 times.

Precautions: Sheetali and seetkari should not be practised in a dirty, polluted atmosphere or during cold weather.

Benefits: As for sheetali pranayama.

Bhramari Pranayama (humming bee breath)

Sit in any comfortable asana with the spine erect, head straight, and both knees resting on the floor.

Close the eyes and relax the whole body for a few moments.

Inhale fully through both nostrils.

Plug the ears with the index fingers and with the teeth apart and the mouth closed, exhale completely while producing a humming sound like that of a bee.
Exhalation should be slow and steady.
Concentrate on the humming sound.
Repeat 10 times.

Contra-indications: Bhramari should not be performed while lying down. People suffering from severe ear infections should not practise this pranayama until the infection has cleared up.

Benefits: This practice alleviates tensions caused by anger and anxiety. Bhramari is beneficial for persons with high blood pressure and is very good for the vocal cords. It helps to relieve headaches and sleeplessness. It speeds up the healing of body tissue and may be practised after operations.

Bhastrika Pranayama (bellows breath)

Sit in any comfortable asana with the spine erect and the knees resting on the floor.
Close the eyes and relax the whole body.
Close the right nostril and take 20 rapid respirations through the left nostril.
Repeat 20 through the right nostril.
Then perform the 20 rapid respirations through both nostrils.
Make sure that the inhalation and exhalation are of equal duration and rhythmic.
The nostrils should not expand and contract during the practice, but should be kept still.

Contra-indications: Bhastrika should not be practised by those who suffer from high blood pressure, heart disease, hernia, gastric ulcer, stroke, epilepsy or vertigo.
Those suffering from lung diseases such as asthma and chronic bronchitis or who are recovering from tuberculosis, are recommended to practise bhakstrika only under expert guidance.

Benefits: This practice purifies the lungs by eliminating unwanted carbon dioxide. It relieves inflammation of the throat and increases the gastric fire. It is an effective exercise for the relief and elimination of many lung, throat and chest diseases. It increases the heat in the body.

Twisting and breathing

Sit in the animal relaxation pose (see page 170), however in this practice the palms are brought together, the hands are resting on top of the head and the elbows are out to the sides.

Inhale to the count of four as you gradually twist the upper body towards the left as far as possible.

Exhale to the count of four as you slowly return the body and face the front.

Repeat 5 to 10 times.

Stretch the legs and repeat on the other side.

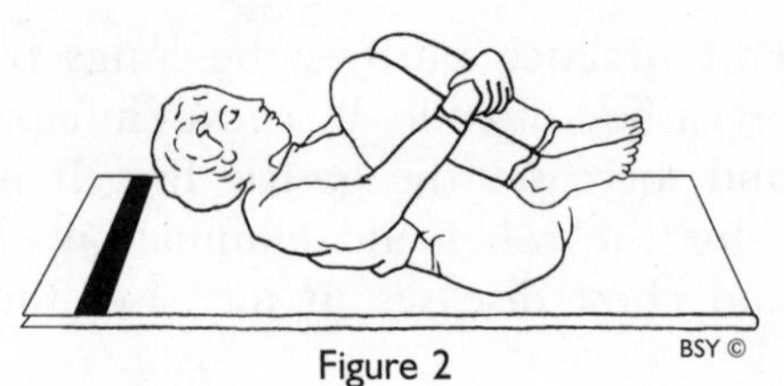

Figure 2

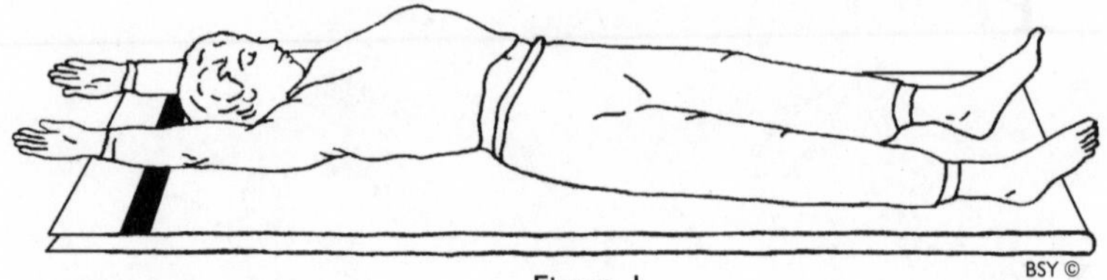

Figure 1

Ha breathing

Lie in shavasana, eyes gently closed.

Inhale slowly and deeply through the nostrils while stretching the arms out on the floor behind the head. (Figure 1)

While exhaling quickly through the mouth and making a '*ha*' sound, bend the knees up against the chest, hugging both legs close to the body. (Figure 2)

Inhale again slowly while straightening the legs back to the floor and stretching the arms above the head.

If necessary take a few natural breaths before repeating 3 more exhalations.

Then while exhaling slowly return the arms to the sides, resuming shavasana and relaxing.

30

Practical Teaching Syllabus*

Swami Satyananda Saraswati

Yoga is not like history or mathematics which can be learned through the intellect and memory alone. It has to be understood and practised with the whole being, and for that there should be at least one exercise which can be performed daily.

Each morning surya namaskara should be practised. The first two mornings can be devoted to teaching the asanas, after which the children should be able to perform the the twelve positions while the teacher simply calls out the numbers. A demonstrator should do the practice with the children for at least two weeks until they learn to do it by themselves. Three rounds of surya namaskara should be performed. One round includes two cycles of the twelve positions, so each position is performed six times in all. After completing the practice everyone should sit down in a comfortable posture, with the spine erect, the head straight and the hands placed either on the knees or in the lap.

For one week the children can practise becoming aware of their breathing. With eyes closed, they are to observe the flow of the breath, to experience it going in and out. After one week they can start the first stage of nadi shodhana pranayama, which is to be continued each morning for the

*In this chapter Swami Satyananda has prescribed fifty lessons to be taught to children aged 12 to 14 for a period of one year.

rest of the year. Two rounds of slow breathing are to be practised, five times through the left nostril and five times through the right nostril. At the time of doing pranayama the children should keep their eyes closed and be aware only of their breath.

There will be fifty lessons during one school year. The teacher needs to be very careful to give equal attention to each child. The children should not overdo any of the practices or strain themselves in any way. If a child cannot perform a particular posture, the teacher should not allow him or her to exert undue force. The teacher has to guide the children and at the same time do the practices with them so that both go through the same experiences. After each class there should always be an opportunity for the children to talk with the teacher in order to discuss any problems or misunderstandings that may arise.

Some hints

- Asanas should be practised on a blanket folded in four or on a mat doubled over, never on the hard, bare floor or on a thin sheet which may slip.
- Loose, light and comfortable clothing should be worn.
- The bladder should preferably be empty before practising asanas and pranayama.
- Asanas and pranayama should be practised when the stomach is empty or at least three hours after meals.
- The children can be encouraged to keep a practical notebook after each lesson and to practise the asanas individually with only a little supervision from the teacher.

LESSON 1

1. **Shavasana**

   Shavasana should be practised before starting asana practice. It is very important that the children relax their bodies and minds completely to avoid straining a nerve or a muscle.

2. **Surya namaskara**

   The first two lessons should be devoted to the practice of surya namaskara in order to perfect it and to avoid future difficulties.

3. **Shavasana**

4. **Breath awareness**

   The children should sit in a comfortable asana, with eyes closed, and observe the flow of their breath for about five minutes.

LESSON 2

1. **Shavasana**
2. **Surya namaskara**
3. **Shavasana**
4. **Breath awareness**

   The children need to be taught how to breathe slowly, by breathing in and out very deeply without raising their chests and without straining their lungs.

LESSON 3

1. **Shavasana**

2. **Surya namaskara**

   Practise two rounds (i.e. four cycles)

3. **Padmasana**

   This posture has to be taught slowly. Children should not try to force their limbs into positions which they find difficult. If the knees do not touch the floor, the muscles should be trained by slowly pushing the knee down with the hand, as in half butterfly and full butterfly. Children who can manage to sit in padmasana should not do so for more than five or six seconds at first. They may then relax their limbs and repeat the posture. When all the children are able to sit in padmasana, they should sit with spines erect, heads up and hands on the knees. Let them compete as to who can sit for one full minute without moving even a single part of the body. The eyes should be kept closed.

4. **Shavasana**
5. **Breath awareness** (with deep breathing)

LESSON 4

Repetition of Lesson 3.

LESSON 5

1. **Shavasana**
2. **Surya namaskara**
   Practise two rounds.
3. **Padmasana**
4. **Yogamudrasana**
   The breathing should be explained carefully. No one should be allowed to retain the breath for a long time. Those who cannot sit in padmasana yet can practise yoga mudrasana in vajrasana instead.

LESSON 6

1. **Shavasana**
2. **Surya namaskara**
   Practise two rounds
3. **Padmasana**
4. **Yoga mudrasana**
5. **Shavasana**
6. **Breath awareness** (with deep breathing)

LESSON 7

1. **Shavasana**
2. **Surya namaskara** (one round)
3. **Padmasana**
4. **Yogamudrasana**

5. **Matsyasana**
   The teacher needs to be careful that the children do not strain. It is advisable to supervise pupils individually and help them to perform the asana correctly.
6. **Shavasana**
7. **Breath awareness** (with deep breathing)

LESSON 8

1. **Shavasana**
2. **Surya namaskara** (one round)
3. **Padmasana**
4. **Yogamudrasana**
5. **Matsyasana**
6. **Shavasana**
7. **Breath awareness** (with deep breathing)

LESSON 9

1. **Shavasana**
2. **Surya namaskara** (one round)
3. **Padmasana**
4. **Yogamudrasana**
5. **Matsyasana**
6. **Baddha padmasana**
   At first the children should try to grasp one big toe with one hand, then the other big toe with the other hand, ultimately grasping both toes at the same time. This asana should not be held for too long without intervals of rest.
7. **Shavasana**
8. **Breath awareness** (with deep breathing)

LESSON 10

1. **Shavasana**
2. **Surya namaskara**
3. **Padmasana**
4. **Yogamudrasana**
5. **Matsyasana**
6. **Baddha padmasana**

7. **Shavasana**
8. **Breath awareness** (with deep breathing)

LESSON 11
1. **Shavasana**
2. **Surya namaskara**
3. **Padmasana**
4. **Yogamudrasana**
5. **Matsyasana**
6. **Baddha padmasana**
7. **Garbha pindasana**
   Children find this asana easy to peform. There should be no forcing of the limbs.
8. **Shavasana**
9. **Nadi shodhana – stage I** (one round)

LESSON 12
Repetition of Lesson 11.

LESSON 13
1. **Shavasana**
2. **Surya namaskara**
3. **Padmasana**
4. **Yogamudrasana**
5. **Matsyasana**
6. **Baddha padmasana**
7. **Garbha pindasana**
8. **Kukkutasana**
9. **Shavasana**
10. **Nadi shodhana – stage I** (two rounds)

LESSON 14
Repetition of Lesson 13.

LESSON 15
1. **Shavasana**
2. **Surya namaskara**

3. **Padmasana**
4. **Yogamudrasana**
5. **Matsyasana**
6. **Baddha padmasana**
7. **Garbha pindasana**
8. **Kukkutasana**
9. **Lolasana**
10. **Shavasana**
11. **Nadi shodhana – stage 1** (two rounds)

LESSON 16
Repetition of Lesson 15.

LESSON 17
1. **Shavasana**
2. **Surya namaskara**
3. **Padmasana**
4. **Yogamudrasana**
5. **Matsyasana**
6. **Baddha padmasana**
7. **Garbha pindasana**
8. **Kukkutasana**
9. **Lolasana**
10. **Vajrasana**
    The children should be encouraged to sit in vajrasana at home for five to ten minutes after each meal. The reason should be explained to them.
11. **Shavasana**
12. **Nadi shodhana – stage 1** (two rounds)
    stage 2 (four rounds)

LESSON 18
Repetition of Lesson 17.

LESSON 19
1. **Shavasana**
2. **Surya namaskara**

3. **Padmasana**
4. **Yogamudrasana**
5. **Matsyasana**
6. **Baddha padmasana**
7. **Garbha pindasana**
8. **Kukkutasana**
9. **Lolasana**
10. **Vajrasana**
11. **Supta vajrasana**
12. **Shavasana**
13. **Nadi shodhana – stage 1** (two rounds)
    stage 2 (five rounds)
14. **Bhramari pranayama** (three rounds)

LESSON 20

Repetition of Lesson 19.

LESSON 21

1. **Shavasana**
2. **Surya namaskara**
3. **Padmasana**
4. **Yogamudrasana**
5. **Matsyasana**
6. **Baddha padmasana**
7. **Garbha pindasana**
8. **Kukkutasana**
9. **Lolasana**
10. **Vajrasana**
11. **Supta vajrasana**
12. **Shashankasana**
13. **Shavasana**
14. **Nadi shodhana – stage 1** (two rounds)
    stage 2 (five rounds)
15. **Bhramari pranayama** (three rounds)

LESSON 22

Repetition of Lesson 21.

LESSON 23

Repeat 1–12 as in Lesson 21.

13. **Simhasana**

    Children laugh when they first do this posture. It should then be explained to them how good simhasana is for their tonsils and that they should practise in the morning, sitting outside just as the sun rises, letting the rays of the sun shine into their throats.
14. **Shavasana**
15. **Nadi shodhana**
16. **Bhramari**

LESSON 24

Repetition of Lesson 23.

LESSON 25

Repeat 1–13 as in Lesson 23.

14. **Paschimottanasana**
15. **Shavasana**
16. **Nadi shodhana**
17. **Bhramari**

LESSON 26

Repetition of Lesson 25.

LESSON 27

Repeat 1–14 as in Lesson 25.

15. **Makarasana**
16. **Shavasana**
17. **Nadi shodhana**
18. **Bhramari**
19. **Sheetali**

LESSON 28

Repetition of Lesson 27.

LESSON 29

Repeat 1–15 as in Lesson 27.

16. **Naukasana**

    The children should not be allowed to hold their breath longer than is comfortable.

17. **Shavasana**
18. **Nadi shodhana**
19. **Bhramari**
20. **Sheetali**

LESSON 30

Repetition of Lesson 29.

LESSON 31

Repeat 1–16 as in Lesson 29.

17. **Sarvangasana**

    The teacher will need to decide how long each child should perform this posture. Normally developed and healthy children should not practise it for more than a few seconds. Underdeveloped children should practise it from one to five minutes, increasing the time very gradually in successive practices.

18. **Shavasana**
19. **Nadi shodhana**
20. **Bhramari**
21. **Sheetali**

LESSON 32

Repetition of Lesson 31.

LESSON 33

Repeat 1–17 as in Lesson 31.

18. **Halasana**
19. **Shavasana**
20. **Nadi shodhana**
21. **Bhramari**
22. **Sheetali**

LESSON 34

Repetition of Lesson 33.

LESSON 35

Repeat 1–18 as in Lesson 33.

19. **Ushtrasana**
20. **Shavasana**
21. **Nadi shodhana**
22. **Bhramari**
23. **Sheetali**
24. **Seetkari**

LESSON 36

Repetition of Lesson 35.

LESSON 37

Repeat 1–19 as in Lesson 35.

20. **Ardha matsyendrasana**
21. **Shavasana**
22. **Nadi shodhana**
23. **Bhramari**
24. **Sheetali**
25. **Seetkari**

LESSON 38

Repetition of Lesson 37.

LESSON 39

Repeat 1–20 as in Lesson 37.

21. **Bhujangasana**
22. **Shavasana**
23. **Nadi shodhana**
24. **Bhramari**
25. **Sheetali**
26. **Seetkari**

LESSON 40
Repetition of Lesson 39.

LESSON 41
Repeat 1–21 as in Lesson 39.
22. **Shalabhasana**
23. **Shavasana**
24. **Nadi shodhana**
25. **Bhramari**
26. **Sheetali**
27. **Seetkari**

LESSON 42
Repetition of Lesson 41.

LESSON 43
Repeat 1–22 as in Lesson 41.
23. **Dhanurasana**
24. **Shavasana**
25. **Nadi shodhana**
26. **Bhramari**
27. **Sheetali**
28. **Seetkari**
29. **Bhastrika**
    Practise ten rapid breaths with the left nostril then with the right nostril.

LESSON 44
Repetition of Lesson 43.

LESSON 45
Repeat 1–23 as in Lesson 43.
24. **Tadasana**
25. **Shavasana**
26. **Nadi shodhana**
27. **Bhramari**
28. **Sheetali**

29. **Seetkari**
30. **Bhastrika**
    Perform ten rapid breaths through each nostril, then ten rapid breaths through both nostrils.

LESSON 46
Repetition of Lesson 45.

LESSON 47
Repeat 1–24 as in Lesson 45.
25. **Trikonasana**
26. **Shavasana**
27. **Nadi shodhana**
28. **Bhramari**
29. **Sheetali**
30. **Seetkari**
31. **Bhastrika**

LESSON 48
Repetition of Lesson 47.

LESSON 49
1. **Shavasana**
2. **Surya namaskara**
3. **Padmasana**
4. **Yogamudrasana**
5. **Matsyasana**
6. **Baddha padmasana**
7. **Garbha pindasana**
8. **Kukkutasana**
9. **Lolasana**
10. **Vajrasana**
11. **Supta vajrasana**
12. **Shashankasana**
13. **Simhasana**
14. **Paschimottanasana**
15. **Makarasana**

16. **Naukasana**
17. **Sarvangasana**
18. **Halasana**
19. **Ushtrasana**
20. **Ardha matsyendrasana**
21. **Bhujangasana**
22. **Shalabhasana**
23. **Dhanurasana**
24. **Tadasana**
25. **Trikonasana**
26. **Garudasana**
27. **Shavasana**
28. **Nadi shodhana**
29. **Bhramari**
30. **Sheetali**
31. **Seetkari**
32. **Bhastrika**

LESSON 50

Repetition of Lesson 49.

Light of Existen

KAIVALYA	99 NO KLESHAS	98 NIRBEEJA SAMADHI	97 AVIDYA	96 TIMELESSNESS	95 RESIDUAL SAMSKARAS	94 OMNIPO
81 INTOXICATION THROUGH SADHANA	82 KNOWLEDGE OF PAST LIVES	83 HYPNOTISM	84 CHAYA PURUSHA	85 DIVINE BODY	86 SOUND AWARENESS	87 UNIVE BROTHE
80 VAIRAGYA	79 SECRET CRAVING	78 BEAUTIFUL BODY	77 MANTRA SIDDHI	76 CURING DISEASES	75 RITAMBHARA PRAJNA	74 NO PAT
61 GIVING UP SWADHARMA	62 INERT SAMADHI	63 MIND OVER MATTER	64 DEVELOPED AWARENESS	65 LOSS OF EFFORT	66 KNOWLEDGE WITHOUT BOOKS	67 NO DIS
60 GURU	59 EGO	58 TAPAS	57 DISCRIMINATION	56 NON-POSSESSION	55 TRUTHFULNESS	54 BRAHMA
41 TUBERCULOSIS	42 DEPENDENCY	43 BLACK MAGIC	44 SELF-KNOWLEDGE	45 SUPPRESSION OF EMOTIONS	46 DRY HEART	47 WISE CO
40 SHRADDHA	39 GURU SEVA	38 INTOXICANTS	37 SERVICE TO PARENTS	36 ANGER	35 SWADHARMA	34 PRI
21 ELOQUENCE	22 LOGIC	23 DEBATE	24 FLIRTATION	25 JEALOUSY	26 PLEASURE	27 HATR
20 COMPLACENCY	19 ATTACHMENT	18 DELUSION	17 ASTHMA	16 LOVE OF MYSTICISM	15 LOVE OF MONEY	14 SERV TO WO
1 SPHOTA	2 MAYA	3 PSEUDO-INTELLECT	4 CRAFTINESS	5 INADEQUACY	6 GREED	7 GUI

nce

ENCE	93 OMNISCIENCE	92 SELF-AWARENESS	91 UNIVERSAL LOVE
SAL HOOD	88 PAPA PURUSHA	89 MASTERY OF ELEMENTS	90 CRUELTY
ENCE	73 SELF-INQUIRY	72 FANATICISM	71 KNOWLEDGE OF DHARMA
ASES	68 LANGUAGE OF BIRDS & ANIMALS	69 KNOWLEDGE OF ARTS	70 SECRET WEAPONS
HARYA	53 TAMAS	52 SELFISHNESS	51 ISHTA
MPANY	48 SCRIPTURAL KNOWLEDGE	49 TASTE OF NECTAR	50 AKASHIC MEMORY
E	33 BHAKTI	32 FAITH IN SCRIPTURES	31 FAITH IN DEITIES
ED	28 AMBITION	29 GAMBLING	30 ENQUIRY
CE MEN	13 FEAR OF DEATH	12 NON-VIOLENCE	11 INDULGENCE
T	8 SKIN DISEASE	9 LAZINESS	10 SELF-RESTRAINT

31

Light of Existence Explained

The game 'Light of Existence' or 'Samsaar Deep' has been adapted from 'Snakes and Ladders' (see insert). It demonstrates the spiritual path, the way in which different qualities either help or cause the downfall of the player travelling according to the throw of a dice. The game has been constructed strictly in accordance with scriptural advice. The meaning of the terms is explained here, and the scriptural references (or other sources which have given the guidelines for the construction of the game) are stated.

One dice is used. Throwing a six means an extra throw. To experience the real endurance required, you have to keep moving backwards and forwards along the top line (once you are lucky enough to be there), risking the snakes of avidya and residual samskaras which plunge the most advanced players back into maya and inertia, until you find the exact number for kaivalya. *Keep moving*.

Explanation of each number

1. **Sphota** – a word from the Shaivism texts of Kashmiri origin, its literal meaning is the first 'big bang' of creation when Brahman became manifest and *Aum* began.
2. **Maya** – delusion, its function is to hide things which exist and show unreal things.
3. **Lokik buddhi** – pseudo-intellect.
4. **Kutilata** – craftiness.

5. **Aparyaptata** – inadequacy.
6. **Lobha** – greed.
7. **Aparadha bhavana** – guilt.
8. **Charmarog** – skin disease.
9. **Alasya** – laziness.
10. **Dama** – self-restraint.
11. **Atibhoga** – indulgence.
12. **Ahimsa** – non-violence.
13. **Mritubhaya** – fear of death.
14. **Stri seva** – service to women.
15. **Dhana prem** – love of money.
16. **Atma ruchi** – love of mysticism.
17. **Damaa** – asthma.
18. **Moha** – delusion.
19. **Raga** – attachment.
20. **Mana shaithilya** – complacency.
21. **Vak patuta** – eloquence.
22. **Tarka** – logic.
23. **Vad vivad** – debating.
24. **Ishkabaji** – flirtation.
25. **Irsha** – jealousy.
26. **Sukha bhav** – pleasure.
27. **Dwesha** – hatred.
28. **Mahattwakamksha** – ambition.
29. **Juna** – gambling.
30. **Vicharan** (shodh) – enquiry.
31. **Devato mei shraddha** – faith in deities.
32. **Shastra mei shraddha** – faith in scriptures.
33. **Bhakti** – devotion to God.
34. **Dambha** – pride.
35. **Swadharma** – one's own duty.
36. **Krodha** – anger.
37. **Matri pitri seva** – service to parents.
38. **Nasha** – intoxicants.
39. **Guru seva** – service of guru.
40. **Shraddha** – faith.
41. **Saahayarog** – tuberculosis.
42. **Para nirbharata** – dependency.

43. **Abhichar** – black magic.
44. **Vijnana** – self-knowledge.
45. **Bhavanatmaka damana** – suppression of emotions.
46. **Shushata** – dry heart.
47. **Satsang** – wise company.
48. **Shastra jnana** – scriptural knowledge.
49. **Amrit swad** – taste of nectar.
50. **Divya smriti** – akashic memory.
51. **Ishta** – one's goal in life.
52. **Swardha** – selfishness.
53. **Tamas** – mental inertia.
54. **Brahmacharya** – celibacy.
55. **Satya** – truthfulness.
56. **Aparigraha** – non-possession.
57. **Viveka** – discrimination between real and unreal.
58. **Tapas** – austerity.
59. **Ahamkara** – ego.
60. **Guru** – dispeller of darkness.
61. **Dharma tyaga** – giving up swadharma (one's duty).
62. **Jhar samadhi** – inert samadhi.
63. **Prakamya** – mind over matter.
64. **Pratibha** – developed consciousness.
65. **Viphal prayatna** – loss of effort.
66. **Antar jnana** – inner understanding.
67. **Ragamukti** – no diseases.
68. **Pashyanti** – the third state of sound.
69. **Kala jnana** – knowledge of arts.
70. **Galat shastra prayog** – secret weapons.
71. **Dharma jnana** – knowledge of duty.
72. **Apurna jnana** – half-knowledge, which causes fanaticism.
73. **Atmanusandhan** – self-enquiry.
74. **Nidhaiya** – no patience.
75. **Ritambhara prajna** – fullness of experience.
76. **Dhanvantari darshan** – vision of the doctor of the gods.
77. **Mantra siddhi** – perfection in the use of mystic syllables.
78. **Roopa lavanya** – beautiful body.
79. **Gupta kamabhai** – secret craving.
80. **Vairagya** – spirit of renunciation.

81. **Sadhana ki nasha** – intoxication through sadhana.
82. **Jati smaran** – knowledge of past lives.
83. **Vashikarana** – hypnotism.
84. **Chhaya purusha** – symbol of lower intellect or wordly intellect.
85. **Divya deha** – divine body.
86. **Nada chaitanya** – sound awareness.
87. **Vishwa bhratritva** – universal brotherhood.
88. **Papa purusha** – symbol of sin, guilt-consciousness.
89. **Tanmatra siddhi** – mastery of elements.
90. **Krurata** – cruelty.
91. **Vishwa prem** – universal love.
92. **Atmajnana** – self-awareness.
93. **Sarva gyattwa** – omniscience.
94. **Anantavirya** – omnipotence.
95. **Samskara shesha** – deep-rooted tendencies of the mind.
96. **Animesh** – timelessness.
97. **Avidya** – ignorance of ultimate truth.
98. **Nirbeeja samadhi** – state of perfect concentration.
99. **Klesharahita** – absolutely no suffering.
100. **Kaivalya** – cosmic consciousness.

How to play

To understand the connections between the states read on. If you land on a snake you travel downwards. If on an arrow you go upwards.

Snakes

97: avidya to 2: maya – *Patanjali* 2:24 (implied)
95: residual samskaras to 62: inert samadhi – *Teachings of Sri Ramakrishna Paramahamsa*
90: cruelty to 13: fear of death – *Puranas*
88: papa purusha to 53: tamas – *Rig Veda, Tattwa Shuddhi*
83: hypnostism to 41: tuberculosis – *Mahabharata*
81: intoxication through sadhana to 46: dry heart – *Teachings of Swami Satyananda Saraswati, Meditations from the Tantras* and *Teachings of Brahmananda* (disciple of Ramakrishna)

79: secret craving to 9: laziness – general yoga psychology
74: no patience to 65: loss of effort – *Puranas*
72: fanaticism to 34: pride – *Mahabharata*; *Puranas*
70: secret weapons to 7: guilt – *Mahabharata* (e.g. case of Ashwahama)
61: giving up swadharma to 5: inadequacy – *Puranas*
59: ego to 36: anger – *Mahabharata* (e.g. Duryodhana)
52: selfishness to 3: pseudo-intellect – *Puranas*; general yoga psychology
45: suppression of emotions to 17: asthma – *Sivànanda*: *Karma and Diseases*
43: black magic to 18: delusion – *Puranas*
42: dependency to 20: complacency – from general yoga psychology
38: intoxicants to 19: attachment – general yoga psychology
27: hatred to 4: craftiness – *Mahabharata*, (e.g. Shakuni)
25: jealousy to 6: greed – *Mahabharata* (e.g. Duryodhana and the magic palace)
24: flirtation to 8: skin disease – *Sivananda*: *Karma and Diseases*

Arrows

10: self-restraint to 32: faith in scriptures – *Puranas*
12: non-violence to 91: universal love – *Patanjali* 2:35
14: service to women to 26: pleasure – *Mahabharata*
16: love of mysticism to 47: wise company – *Aparoksha Anubhuti*
30: enquiry to 44: self-knowledge – common sense
33: bhakti to 51: ishta – *Bhakti Sutras*
37: service to parents to 75: ritambhara prajna – *Mahabharata*
39: guru seva to 60: guru – *Padma Purana*, in the *Guru Gita*
54: brahmacharya to 94: omnipotence – *Patanjali* 2:38
55: truthfulness to 73: self-enquiry – *Bhagavata Purana* (implied)
58: tapas to 85: divine body – *Patanjali* 2:43
80: vairagya to 93: omniscience – *Patanjali* 3:50 (implied)

Bibliography

Introduction

Farley, F., Reported by Hooper, J. 'Charts of the Soul', *Omni,* 1983.

Stewart, M.A. 'Hyperactive Children', *Scientific American.*

Chapter 3

Montessori, Dr M. *Education for a New World,* Kalakshetra Publications.

Montessori, Dr M. *The Formation of Man,* Theosophical Publishing House, 1969.

Vygotsky, L.S. 'Play and its Role in the Mental Development of the Child', *Play: Its Role in Development and Evolution.* eds. J. Bruner, A. Jolly & K. Sylva, Penguin Education, 1976.

Jackson, B. 'Living with Children', *Observer Magazine,* 22 Sept. 1974.

Donaldson, M. *Children's Minds,* Fontana Collins, 1978.

Coleman, J.S. 'Learning through Games', *Play: Its Role in Development and Evolution,* eds. J. Bruner, A. Jolly & K. Sylva, Penguin Education, 1976.

Sylva, K. Bruner, J. & Genova, P. 'The Role of Play in Problem Solving of Children 3–5 Years Old', *Play: Its Role in Development and Evolution,* eds. J. Bruner, A. Jolly & K. Sylva, Penguin Education, 1976.

Chapter 7

Smith, J. 'Teachers urged to leave safe ground', *Brain-Mind Bulletin,* vol 2, no. 17, July 18, 1977.

Banyuet, J.P. 'Spectral Analysis of the EEG in Meditation', *Electroenceph. & Clin. Neurophys.,* 1973, 35: 143,151.

Ostrander, S. & Schroeder: ' Mission Control Centre for the Mind-Suggestology', *Psychic Discoveries Behind the Iron Curtain,* Abacus,1973.

Schuster, D., 'Transpersonal Psychology Goes to School', *Brain-Mind Bulletin,* vol. 3, no. 14, June 5, 1977.

'Art Reinforces Cognitive Learning' *Brain-Mind Bulletin,* vol. 2, no. 22, October 3, 1977.

Harlem, S.H. 'Effects of Psychophysiological Relaxation upon Selected Tasks in Urban Elementary School Children', *Diss. Abstra. Int.,* 36 (8-a), 1976.

Chapter 8 & 9

de Culon, Jacques, *Eveil et Harmonie de l'Enfant, Le Yoga a l'Ecole,* Edition Signal Lausanne (2nd edn.) with a foreword by Swami Satyananda Saraswati.

Arganoff, Dr. B. W. & Davis, R. G., University of Michigan.

Chapter 12

Glueck, S. & Glueck, E., *Unravelling Juvenile Delinquency,* Harvard University Press, 1950.

Earle, A. & Earle B., 'Early Maternal Deprivation and Later Psychiatric Illnesses', *American Journal of Orthopsychiatry,* 31, 1961.

Wolff, S. *Children Under Stress,* Pelican Books, 1973.

Chapter 14

Montessori, Dr M. *Discovery of the Child,* Kalakshetra Pub. 1966.

Montessori, Dr M., *What You Should Know About Your Child,* ed. A. G. Prakasam, Kalakshetra Pub. 1966.

Montessori, Dr M., *To Educate the Human Potential,* Kalakshetra Pub. 1967

Levenstein, P. 'Cognitive Development Through Verbalized Play: The Mother Child Home Program'. *Play: Its Role in Development and Evolution,* eds. J. Bruner, A. Jolly and K. Sylva. Penguin Education, 1976.

Miller, S. *The Psychology of Play,* Pelican Original, 1976.

Flavell, J., 'Early and Middle Childhood' *Cognitive Development,* Prentice-Hall Inc. 1977.

Chapters 17 to 31

Swami Satyananda Saraswati, *Asana Pranayama Mudra Bandha,* Bihar Yoga Bharati, Bihar, India, 1996.

Garr, Rachel, *Be A frog, A Bird or A Tree,* Harper Colophon Books, Harper & Row, 1977.

Kent, Howard, *My Fun With Yoga,* Hamlyn Publishing Group Ltd., London 1975.

Luchs, Easter-Martina, *Yoga for Children,* Search Press, London, 1977.

Marshall, Lyn, *Yoga for Your Children,* Ward Lock Ltd., 1978.

Bell, G. H., Emslie-Smith, D. & Paterson, C., *Textbook of Physiology,* Churchill Livingstone, 1980, pp. 508–515.

Index of Practices

A Abdominal Breathing 98, 264
Akarna Dhanurasana (bow and arrow pose) 244
Antar Mouna 99
Ardha Chandra Namaskara 184
Ardha Chandrasana (crescent moon pose) 228
Ardha Matsyendrasana (half spinal twist) 236
Ardha Padma Padmottanasana
(half lotus leg stretch) 256
Ardha Titali Asana (half butterfly) 145
Ardha Ushtrasana (half camel pose) 207
Arjunasana (balanced archer's pose) 252

B Baddha Padmasana (locked lotus pose) 247
Baka Dhyanasana (patient crane pose) 206
Bakasana (crane pose) 211
Balancing on the buttocks 154
Bhastrika Pranayama (bellows breath) 268
Bhramari Pranayama
(humming bee breath) 98, 267
Bhujangasana (cobra pose) 197
Bhumi Pada Mastakasana
(half headstand or letter A) 255
Blossoming lotus 96, 102
Breathing with pictures 121
Bumblebee pose 216

C Chakki Chalanasana (churning the mill) 223
Chakrasana (wheel pose) 226
Chandra Namaskara
(salutations to the moon) 103, 182
Chinese Dragon 260

D Dancing Duo 261
Dhanurakarshanasana (archer's pose) 252
Dhanurasana (bow pose) 225
Dolasana (pendulum pose) 231
Double Windmill 261
Dynamic Paschimottanasana
(back stretch or hairpin pose) 235

E Eka Pada Pranamasana
(one legged prayer or tree pose) 245
Eka Padasana (one foot or letter T pose) 257
Eye Exercises 171

G Garbha Pindasana (foetus in the womb pose) 254
Garudasana (eagle pose) 212
Gayatmak Meru Vakrasana (dynamic spinal twist) 165
Gomukhasana (cow's face pose) 209
Goolf Chakra (ankle rotation) 143
Goolf Ghoornan (ankle crank) 143
Goolf Naman (ankle bending) 143
Greeva Sanchalana (neck movements) 152
Growing tree 115

H Halasana (plough or wheelbarrow pose) 242
Hasta Pada Angushthasana
(finger to toe stretch or fan pose) 234
Hopping Rabbit Pose 219

J Jack Knife Pose 243
Janu Chakra (knee crank) 145
Janu Naman (knee bending) 144
Jhulana Lurhakanasana (rocking and rolling) 157

K Kawa Chalasana (crow walking) 210
Kehuni Naman (elbow bending) 151
Koormasana (tortoise pose) 203
Kukkutasana (cockerel pose) 206

L Leo the friendly lion 214
Lolasana (swinging pose) 247

M Makarasana (crocodile pose) 195
Mandukasana (hopping frog pose) 218
Manibandha Chakra (wrist joint rotation) 150
Manibandha Naman (wrist bending) 149
Marjariasana (cat stretch pose) 204
Matsya Kridasana (flapping fish pose) 194
Matsyasana (fish pose) 196
Mushtika Bandhana (hand clenching) 149

N Nadi Shodhana Pranayama
(alternate nostril breathing) 265
Nadi Shodhana (using hands, arms or legs) 123
Namaskarasana (salutation pose) 166
Natarajasana 1 (Lord Shiva's dance) 250
Natarajasana 2 (Lord Shiva's pose)
Preparatory form 251
Full form 251
Natavarasana (Lord Krishna's pose) 249
Nauka Sanchalanasana (rowing the boat) 222
Naukasana (boat pose) 223

O Ostrich pose 114, 218

P Pada Hastasana
(forward bending or pincer pose) 232
Padanguli Naman (toe bending) 142
Pada Sanchalanasana (cycling) 161
Padmasana (lotus pose) 246
Parambhik Sthiti (base position) 142

Poorna Bhujangasana (full cobra pose) 219
Poorna Chandra Namaskara
(salutations to the full moon) 187
Poorna Titali Asana (full butterfly pose) 212
Potato stop 114
Punctured balloon 120

S Saithalyasana (animal relaxation pose) 170
Sarpasana (snake pose) 202
Sarvangasana (shoulder stand or candle pose) 241
Seetkari Pranayama (hissing breath) 267
Setu Asana (bridge pose) 229
Setu Baddhasana (bound bridge pose) 229
Shalabhasana (locust pose) 199
Shashank Bhujangasana (striking cobra pose) 199
Shashankasana (pose of the moon or hare pose) 162
Shavasana (corpse pose) 193
Sheetali Pranayama (cooling breath) 266
Simhasana (lion pose) 213
Skandha Chakra (shoulder socket rotation) 151
Spinal massage 156
Stambhan Asana (posture of retention) 262
Stop and write 117
Stork pose 217
Sukhasana (easy pose) 155
Sumeru Asana (summit pose) 233
Sun and moon gazing 126
Supta Pawanmuktasana 1 (simple leg lock pose) 158
Supta Pawanmuktasana 2 (leg lock pose) 159
Supta Vajrasana (sleeping thunderbolt pose) 225
Surya Namaskara (salutations to the sun) 103, 176

T Tadasana (palm tree pose) 237
Teapot pose 97, 242
Tibetan purification exercise 111
Tiryaka Bhujangasana (twisting cobra pose) 198
Tiryaka Tadasana (swaying palm tree pose) 238

Trataka (concentrated gazing) 116
Trikonasana (triangle pose) 238–240
Twisting and breathing 269

U Udarakarshanasana (abdominal stretch pose) 168
Ushtrasana (camel pose) 208
Utthan Pristhasana (lizard pose) 201
Utthanasana (squat and rise pose) 169

V Vajrasana (thunderbolt pose) 224
Vajroli Mudra (thunderbolt attitude, letter V
or lapwing pose) 215, 258
Vayu Nishkasana (wind releasing pose) 167
Vrischikasana (scorpion pose) 220
Vyaghrasana (tiger pose) 205

W Warrior sequence 103, 188
Wheelbarrow 259

Y Yoga nidra 99, 127
Yoga zoo 95
Yogamudrasana (psychic union pose) 248

General Index

Acetylcholine 8
Adrenal system 3, 15, 23, 70, 78
Ajna chakra (sixth psychic centre, the seat of intuition) 3, 14–15, 23, 24
Alertness 60, 62
Allergic reactions 32
Alpha waves 19
Alveoli 31
Amphetamines 7–8
Anger 79
Antar mouna 20–21, 99
Antisocial behaviour 69
Archetypes in the brain 66
Arthritis 32
Asanas 3, 42, 46, 65, 84, 88, 102–103, 110–111, 119, 133–138
Ashram life 80, 88, 106–107
Asthma 32
Attention 2, 8, 52, 58, 59, 62–64, 100, 119, 125
Autistic child 86
Awareness 2, 49, 58–60

Behavioural aspect of personality 19, 29
Biochemical 37
Bioenergy 2, 70
Biofeedback 4, 46, 49
Body awareness 97, 99, 110, 135
Brain 2, 8, 14–21, 23, 26, 32, 37, 38, 45–49, 53, 66, 80, 123
Breathing (see also pranayama) 9, 54, 72, 115, 121, 122, 123–125

Cancer 32
Cardiovascular mechanisms 31
Chanting 66, 118
Cognitive development 25–30, 49, 95
Concentration 2, 23, 49, 55, 61, 62, 66, 116, 118, 125–126
Consciousness 3, 8, 14, 18, 21, 24, 28, 32, 37, 44, 45, 47, 58, 63, 72, 82
Creative aspect of personality 2, 5, 26–30, 46, 63, 97

Delinquent children 79
Delta waves 19
Diabetes 87–89
Diet 88, 89, 137
Digestive system 88–89
Disabled children 7–9, 83–86
Discipline 5, 33, 67
Discrimination 37, 70
DNA molecules 68
Dopamine-acetylcholine 8
Dreams 24, 47
Dull mind 15–16, 19

Economic problems 34
Education system 4, 9, 13–21, 33, 34–38, 47–48
Ego 32
Electrical activities 19
Emotional aspect of personality 2, 4, 8, 23, 24, 29,33, 42, 80, 100
Emotionally disturbed children 4, 7, 8–9, 14, 73, 77–82, 89
Emotional stability 7, 9, 15, 23, 25, 42
Endocrine system 2, 3, 7, 8, 23, 32, 33, 38, 89

Games 28–30, 104
Gayatri mantra 22, 31, 65
Gonads 19
Group atmosphere 60, 112
Group awareness 118
Gurukul system 67

Hatha yoga 18, 38, 119
Heart 32, 86, 88
Hormonal imbalances 2, 3, 19
Hormonal secretions 2, 8, 32
Hormones 19, 59, 70, 80
Hypersensitivity diseases 32
Hyperactive child 7–8, 81

Ida nadi 3, 18, 47, 80, 81, 23
Imagination 28, 108, 121
Immune deficiency diseases (see Asthma, Arthritis) 32
Immune surveillance system 31
Intellect 33, 37, 49, 71, 72, 95
Intuition 3, 5, 33, 46, 48, 80

Jaundice 88
Joints 2, 141
Juvenile delinquents 69–71, 79
Juvenile diabetes 87–89

Karma yoga (yoga of selfless actions) 7, 33, 79
Kirtan 65, 85, 100
Kriya yoga 46
Kumbhaka 72

Liver 88
Lungs 2, 3, 31–32

Mammary glands 24
Manas shakti 80
Mandala 135
Mantra 18, 21, 24, 31, 53, 65, 66, 71–72
Meditation 21, 46, 47, 48, 49, 116, 125
Medulla oblongata 23, 80
Memory 21, 47, 49, 58, 66, 116, 119, 126
Mental aspect of personality 4, 15, 23, 26–30, 38, 42, 49, 72
Mental energy 4, 18, 37, 80

Mentally disabled 7, 83–86
Metabolism 3
Moral behaviour 15, 23, 32
Motionlessness 113, 114
Mudras 23, 24, 38, 81
Muscles 2, 6, 49
Music 48, 66, 94

Nada yoga 119
Nature of child 52
Nervous system 3, 7, 23, 38, 69, 72, 80, 81, 93
Neurotransmitters 8, 59
Noradrenalin 9

Om 53, 118
Ovaries 24
Oxygen 2, 53

Pancreas 88–89
Parasympathetic nervous system 80
Pawanmuktasana 139–160
Physical aspect of personality 2, 23, 26, 38, 42
Physical education 6, 7, 18
Pineal gland (see also ajna chakra) 3, 6, 14, 15, 23–24, 70, 71, 80, 123
Pingala nadi 3, 18, 47, 80, 81, 123
Pituitary 3, 15, 32, 69, 80
Play 28–30, 33
Political problems 34
Prana 3, 4, 18, 70
Prana shakti 80
Pranayama 2, 3, 8, 9, 18–19, 22, 24, 31, 38, 42, 46, 65, 107, 123
Pranic channel 47
Pranic energy 19, 46, 52, 63, 79
Pratyahara 2
Pregnancy (intra-uterine life) 25, 31, 68, 88–89
Preventative medicine 47
Problem solving 29
Progressive evolutionary movement 4, 36
Psychic personality 47
Psycho-emotional balance 9, 19–24
Psychomotor normality 8
Psychophysiology 2, 4, 6, 18–21, 23, 31–33, 37, 53–55
Puberty 3, 32–33, 37, 39–44, 65, 69–70

Rajasic 62, 63
Receptive minds 14
Relaxation training (see also yoga nidra) 49, 88, 94, 107, 120, 127, 136
Representation competence 94
Respiratory mechanisms 31

Salivary glands 89
Samadhi 2
Sandhya 65
Sattwic 62, 63
Self-discipline 2, 56, 69, 70
Senses (see also auditory perception, touch, sight) 60
Sex hormones 23
Sexual awareness 3, 24, 32, 66, 69, 70, 80
Shakti bandhas 165–170
Shakti of viveka 70
Shatkriyas 88

Sight 121, 137, 171–175
Social development 7, 29, 40
Social problems 34–38, 39–44
Spinal column 2, 18, 63, 114, 137
Spinal cord 7, 14, 47
Spiritual development 33, 42, 43, 67
Stress 2, 29, 80, 89
Suggestopaedia 60
Sushumna nadi 47
Symbolic vibrations 21
Sympathetic nervous system 3, 80

T'ai chi chuan 47
Tamasic 62, 63
Teaching reading and writing 48
Thymus gland 32
Thyroid 3, 19, 23, 70
Touch 117, 118, 121
Toxins 71
Transpersonal psychology 4, 47
Trataka 116
Tumour 32
Upanayanviddhi ceremony 22, 31
Uterus 24

Visualization 24, 48, 65, 73, 99, 119, 127
Verbal development 95

Yantra 66, 73
Yoga at school 50–56, 57, 131
Yoga in the classroom 50
Yoga nidra 2, 17, 47, 80, 82, 99, 109
Yoga shastras 47
Yoga zoo 95–96

SYNOPSIS OF THE LIFE OF SWAMI SATYANANDA SARASWATI

Swami Satyananda Saraswati was born in 1923 at Almora (Uttaranchal) into a family of farmers. His ancestors were warriors and many of his kith and kin down the line, including his father, served in the army and police force.

However, it became evident that Sri Swamiji had a different bent of mind, as he began to have spiritual experiences at the age of six, when his awareness spontaneously left the body and he saw himself lying motionless on the floor. Many saints and sadhus blessed him and reassured his parents that he had a very developed awareness. This experience of disembodied awareness continued, which led him to many saints of that time such as Anandamayi Ma. Sri Swamiji also met a tantric bhairavi, Sukhman Giri, who gave him shaktipat and directed him to find a guru in order to stabilize his spiritual experiences.

In 1943, at the age of 20, he renounced his home and went in search of a guru. This search ultimately led him to Swami Sivananda Saraswati at Rishikesh, who initiated him into the Dashnam Order of Sannyasa on 12th September 1947 on the banks of the Ganges and gave him the name Swami Satyananda Saraswati.

In those early years at Rishikesh, Sri Swamiji immersed himself in guru seva. At that time the ashram was still in its infancy and even the basic amenities such as buildings and toilets were absent. The forests surrounding the small ashram were infested with snakes, scorpions, mosquitoes, monkeys and even tigers. The ashram work too was heavy and hard, requiring Sri Swamiji to toil like a labourer carrying bucket loads of water from the Ganga up to the ashram and digging canals from the high mountain streams down to the ashram many kilometres away in order to store water for constructing the ashram.

Rishikesh was then a small town and all the ashram requirements had to be brought by foot from far away. In addition there were varied duties, including the daily pooja at Vishwanath

Mandir, for which Sri Swamiji would go into the dense forests to collect bael leaves. If anyone fell sick there was no medical care and no one to attend to them. All the sannyasins had to go out for bhiksha or alms as the ashram did not have a mess or kitchen.

Of that glorious time when he lived and served his guru, Sri Swamiji says that it was a period of total communion and surrender to the guru tattwa, whereby he felt that just to hear, speak or see Swami Sivananda was yoga. But most of all his guru's words rang true, for through this dedication and spirit of nishkama seva he gained an enlightened understanding of the secrets of spiritual life and became an authority on Yoga, Tantra, Vedanta, Samkhya and kundalini yoga. Swami Sivananda said of Swami Satyananda, "Few would exhibit such intense vairagya at such an early age. Swami Satyananda is full of Nachiketa vairagya."

Although he had a photographic memory and a keen intellect, and his guru described him as a versatile genius, Swami Satyananda's learning did not come from books and study in the ashram. His knowledge unfolded from within through his untiring seva as well as his abiding faith and love for Swami Sivananda, who told him,"Work hard and you will be purified. You do not have to search for the light, the light will unfold from within you."

In 1956, after spending twelve years in guru seva, Swami Satyananda set out as a wanderer (parivrajaka). Before his departure Swami Sivananda taught him kriya yoga and gave him the mission to "spread yoga from door to door and shore to shore".

As a wandering sannyasin, Swami Satyananda travelled extensively by foot, car, train and sometimes even by camel throughout India, Afghanistan, Burma, Nepal, Tibet, Ceylon and the entire Asian subcontinent. During his sojourns, he met people from all stratas of society and began formulating his ideas on how to spread the yogic techniques. Although his formal education and spiritual tradition was that of Vedanta, the task of disseminating yoga became his movement.

His mission unfolded before him in 1956 when he founded the International Yoga Fellowship Movement with the aim of creating a global fraternity of yoga. Because his mission was revealed to him at Munger, Bihar, he established the Bihar School of Yoga in Munger. Before long his teachings were rapidly spreading throughout the world. From 1963 to 1983, Swami Satyananda took yoga to each and every corner of the world, to people of every caste, creed, religion and nationality. He guided millions of seekers in all continents and established centres and ashrams in different countries.

His frequent travels took him to Australia, New Zealand, Japan, China, the Philippines, Hong Kong, Malaysia, Thailand, Singapore, USA, England, Ireland, France, Italy, Germany, Switzerland, Denmark, Sweden, Yugoslavia, Poland, Hungary, Bulgaria, Slovenia, Russia, Czechoslovakia, Greece, Saudi Arabia, Kuwait, Bahrain, Dubai, Iraq, Iran, Pakistan, Afghanistan, Colombia, Brazil, Uruguay, Chile, Argentina, Santo Domingo, Puerto Rico, Sudan, Egypt, Nairobi, Ghana, Mauritius, Alaska and Iceland. One can easily say that Sri Swamiji hoisted the flag of yoga in every nook and cranny of the world.

Nowhere did he face opposition, resistance or criticism. His way was unique. Well-versed in all religions and scriptures, he incorporated their wisdom with such a natural flair that people of all faiths were drawn to him. His teaching was not just confined to yoga but covered the wisdom of many millenniums.

Sri Swamiji brought to light the knowledge of Tantra, the mother of all philosophies, the sublime truths of Vedanta, the Upanishads and Puranas, Buddhism, Jainism, Sikhism, Zoroastrianism, Islam and Christianity, including modern scientific analysis of matter and creation. He interpreted, explained and gave precise, accurate and systematic explanations of the ancient systems of Tantra and Yoga, revealing practices hitherto unknown.

It can be said that Sri Swamiji was a pioneer in the field of yoga because his presentation had a novelty and freshness. Ajapa japa, antar mouna, pawanmuktasana, kriya yoga and prana vidya are just some of the practices which he introduced in such a methodical and simple manner that it became possible for everyone to delve into this valuable and hitherto inaccessible science for their physical, mental, emotional and spiritual development.

Yoga nidra was Sri Swamiji's interpretation of the tantric system of nyasa. With his deep insight into this knowledge, he was able to realize the potential of this practice of nyasa in a manner which gave it a practical utility for each and every individual, rather than just remaining a prerequisite for worship. Yoga nidra is but one example of his acumen and penetrating insight into the ancient systems.

Sri Swamiji's outlook was inspiring, uplifting as well as in-depth and penetrating. Yet his language and explanations were always simple and easy to comprehend. During this period he authored over eighty books on yoga and tantra which, due to their authenticity, are accepted as textbooks in schools and universities throughout the world. These books have been translated into Italian, German, Spanish, Russian, Yugoslavian, Chinese, French, Greek, Iranian and most other prominent languages of the world.

People took to his ideas and spiritual seekers of all faiths and nationalities flocked to him. He initiated thousands into mantra and sannyasa, sowing in them the seed to live the divine life. He exhibited tremendous zeal and energy in spreading the light of yoga, and in the short span of twenty years Sri Swamiji fulfilled the mandate of his guru.

By 1983, Bihar School of Yoga was well established and recognized throughout the world as a reputed and authentic centre for learning yoga and the spiritual sciences. More than that, yoga had moved out of the caves of hermits and ascetics into the mainstream of society. Whether in hospitals, jails, schools, colleges, business houses, the sporting and fashion arenas, the army or navy, yoga was in demand. Professionals such as lawyers, engineers, doctors, business magnates and professors were incorporating yoga into their lives. So too were the masses. Yoga had become a household word.

Now, at the peak of his accomplishment, having fulfilled his guru's wish, Swami Satyananda renounced all that he created and appointed his successor, Swami Niranjanananda, to continue the work.

In 1988 Sri Swamiji renounced disciples, establishments and institutions, and departed from Munger, never to return again, on a pilgrimage through the siddha teerthas of India, as a mendicant, without any personal belongings or assistance from the ashrams or institutions he had founded.

At Trayambakeshwar, the jyotir linga of Lord Mrityunjaya, his ishta devata, he renounced his garb and lived as an avadhoota, during which time his future place of abode and sadhana were revealed to him.

According to the mandate of his ishta devata, which was revealed to him at the source of the Godavari river near Neel Parbat at Trayambakeshwar (Maharashtra), Swami Satyananda came to the cremation ground of Sati in 1989, and took up residence in Rikhia, on the outskirts of Baba Baidyanath Dham in Deoghar (Jharkhand).

Swami Satyananda has been residing at Rikhia since September 1989. During this period he has undertaken long and arduous sadhanas such as Panchagni and Ashtottar-shat-laksh (108 lakh) mantra purascharana. Here he entered the lifestyle of the Paramahamsas who do not work for their flock and mission alone but have a universal vision. He does not associate with any institutions, nor does he give diksha, upadesh or receive dakshina, but remains in seclusion and sadhana, only on rare occasions coming out to give darshan to devotees who are always yearning for a glimpse of him.

INTERNATIONAL YOGA FELLOWSHIP MOVEMENT (IYFM)

The IYFM is a charitable and philosophical movement founded by Swami Satyananda at Rajnandgaon in 1956 to disseminate the yogic tradition throughout the world. It forms the medium to convey the teachings of Swami Satyananda through its affiliated centres around the world. Swami Niranjanananda is the first Paramacharya of the International Yoga Fellowship Movement.

The IYFM provides guidance, systematized yoga training programs and sets teaching standards for all the affiliated yoga teachers, centres and ashrams. A Yoga Charter to consolidate and unify the humanitarian efforts of all sannyasin disciples, yoga teachers, spiritual seekers and well-wishers was introduced during the World Yoga Convention in 1993. Affiliation to this Yoga Charter enables the person to become a messenger of goodwill and peace in the world, through active involvement in various far-reaching yoga-related projects.

BIHAR SCHOOL OF YOGA (BSY)

The Bihar School of Yoga is a charitable and educational institution founded by Swami Satyananda at Munger in 1963, with the aim of imparting yogic training to all nationalities and to provide a focal point for a mass return to the ancient science of yoga. The Chief Patron of Bihar School of Yoga is Swami Niranjanananda. The original school, Sivanandashram, is the centre for the Munger locality. Ganga Darshan, the new school established in 1981, is situated on a historic hill with panoramic views of the river Ganges.

Yoga Health Management, Teacher Training, Sadhana, Kriya Yoga and other specialized courses are held throughout the year. BSY is also renowned for its sannyasa training and the initiation of female and foreign sannyasins.

BSY provides trained sannyasins and teachers for conducting yoga conventions, seminars and lectures tours around the world. It also contains a comprehensive research library and scientific research centre.

SIVANANDA MATH (SM)

Sivananda Math is a social and charitable institution founded by Swami Satyananda at Munger in 1984, in memory of his guru, Swami Sivananda Saraswati of Rishikesh. The Head Office is now situated at Rikhia in Deoghar district, Jharkhand. Swami Niranjanananda is the Chief Patron.

Sivananda Math aims to facilitate the growth of the weaker and underprivileged sections of society, especially rural communities. Its activities include: distribution of free scholarships, clothing, farm animals and food, the digging of tube-wells and construction of houses for the needy, assistance to farmers in ploughing and watering their fields. The Rikhia complex also houses a satellite dish system for providing global information to the villagers.

A medical clinic has been established for the provision of medical treatment, advice and education. Veterinary services are also provided. All services are provided free and universally to everyone, regardless of caste and creed.

YOGA RESEARCH FOUNDATION (YRF)

The Yoga Research Foundation is a scientific, research-oriented institution founded by Swami Satyananda at Munger in 1984. Swami Niranjanananda is the Chief Patron of the foundation.

YRF aims to provide an accurate assessment of the practices of different branches of yoga within a scientific framework, and to establish yoga as an essential science for the development of mankind. At present the foundation is working on projects in the areas of fundamental research and clinical research. It is also studying the effects of yoga on proficiency improvement in various social projects, e.g. army, prisoners, children. These projects are being carried out in affiliated centres worldwide.

YRF's future plans include literary, scriptural, medical and scientific investigations into other little-known aspects of yoga for physical health, mental well-being and spiritual upliftment.

SRI PANCHDASHNAM PARAMAHAMSA ALAKH BARA (PPAB)

Sri Panchdashnam Paramahamsa Alakh Bara was established in 1990 by Swami Satyananda at Rikhia, Deoghar, Jharkhand. It is a charitable, educational and non-profit making institution aiming to uphold and propagate the highest tradition of sannyasa, namely vairagya (dispassion), tyaga (renunciation) and tapasya (austerity). It propounds the tapovan style of living adopted by the rishis and munis of the vedic era and is intended only for sannyasins, renunciates, ascetics, tapasvis and paramahamsas. The Alakh Bara does not conduct any activities such as yoga teaching or preaching of any religion or religious concepts. The guidelines set down for the Alakh Bara are based on the classical vedic tradition of sadhana, tapasya and swadhyaya, or atma chintan.

Swami Satyananda, who resides permanently at the Alakh Bara, has performed the Panchagni Vidya and other vedic sadhanas, thus paving the way for future paramahamsas to uphold their tradition.

BIHAR YOGA BHARATI (BYB)

Bihar Yoga Bharati was founded by Swami Niranjanananda in 1994 as an educational and charitable institution for advanced studies in yogic sciences. It is the culmination of the vision of Swami Sivananda and Swami Satyananda. BYB is the world's first accredited institution wholly devoted to teaching yoga. A comprehensive yogic education is imparted with provision to grant certificates and diplomas in yogic studies. It offers a complete scientific and yogic education according to the needs of today, through the areas of Yoga Philosophy, Yoga Psychology, Applied Yogic Science and Yogic Ecology.

Residential courses of four months to one year are conducted in a gurukul environment, so that along with yoga education, the spirit of seva (selfless service), samarpan (dedication) and karuna (compassion) for humankind is also imbibed by the students.

YOGA PUBLICATIONS TRUST (YPT)

Yoga Publications Trust (YPT) was established by Swami Niranjan-ananda in 2000. It is an organization devoted to the dissemination and promotion of yogic and allied knowledge - psychology (ancient and modern), ecology, medicine, vedic, upanishadic, tantric darshanas, philosophies (Eastern and Western), mysticism and spirituality - nationally and internationally through the distribution of books, magazines, audio and video cassettes and multimedia.

YPT is primarily concerned with publishing textbooks in the areas of yoga philosophy, psychology and applied yogic science, research materials, practice texts and the inspiring talks of eminent spiritual personalities and authors aimed at the upliftment of humanity by means of the eternal yogic knowledge, lifestyle and practice.